VOCABULARY THROUGH PLEASURABLE READING BOOK II

By HAROLD LEVINE

Author of

English Alive
English: A Comprehensive Course
Comprehensive English Review Text
The Joy of Vocabulary
Vocabulary for the College-Bound Student
Vocabulary for the High School Student
Vocabulary Through Pleasurable Reading, Books I and II
Vocabulary and Composition Through Pleasurable Reading,
     Books III, IV, V, and VI

Dedicated to serving

AMSCO SCHOOL PUBLICATIONS, INC.
315 Hudson Street, New York, N.Y. 10013

our nation's youth

When ordering this book, please specify:
either R 152 W *or* VOCABULARY THROUGH PLEASURABLE READING, BOOK II,
WORKBOOK EDITION

ACKNOWLEDGMENTS

Grateful acknowledgment is made to the following sources for having granted permission to reprint copyrighted materials.

Baskervilles Investments Limited, London, England. *Selection 13*. From THE REDHEADED LEAGUE by Sir Arthur Conan Doyle.

E. P. Dutton & Co., Inc. *Selection 15*. From the book HOT ROD by Henry Gregor Felsen. Copyright 1950 by E. P. Dutton & Co., Inc., publishers.

Harper & Row, Publishers, Inc. *Selection 1*. From THE ADVENTURES OF TOM SAWYER by Mark Twain. *Selection 10*. From pages 46–51, excluding illustrations on pages 49 and 50, in OLD YELLER by Fred Gipson. Copyright © 1956 by Fred Gipson.

Houghton Mifflin Company. *Selection 5*. From THE HEART IS A LONELY HUNTER by Carson McCullers. Copyright © 1967 by Carson McCullers.

Alfred A. Knopf, Inc. *Selection 4*. From THE BEST OF CLARENCE DAY by Clarence Day. Copyright 1934, 1935 by Clarence Day. Renewed 1962 by Katherine B. Day.

Charles Scribner's Sons. *Selection 3*. From THE YEARLING, pages 36–38, by Marjorie Kinnan Rawlings. Copyright 1938 Marjorie Kinnan Rawlings; renewal copyright © 1966 Norton Baskin.

The Viking Press, Inc. *Selection 8*. From THE PEARL by John Steinbeck. Copyright 1945 by John Steinbeck. Copyright © renewed 1973 by Elaine Steinbeck and John Steinbeck IV.

ISBN 0-87720-369-5

ABOUT THIS BOOK

It is not necessary for students to have studied *Vocabulary Through Pleasurable Reading—Book I* to use this book. Though Book II continues the work of Book I on a somewhat higher level of challenge, it is nevertheless an independent volume. Whenever a topic discussed in Book I is further developed in this book, it will first be reviewed. Students will therefore be able to learn successfully from this volume even if they have not previously used Book I.

This book has a twofold purpose: To broaden students' vocabulary and to make them better readers. It is based on the conviction that good literature can provide students not merely with pleasure, but also with the vocabulary and reading skills that they vitally need. Accordingly, the heart of each of the sixteen units in this book is an unusually interesting passage from a widely read work, such as *The Adventures of Tom Sawyer*, *Up From Slavery*, *Robinson Crusoe*, *The Pearl*, *An Occurrence at Owl Creek Bridge*, or *Hot Rod*. This carefully chosen passage is the inspiration for all the learning in the unit.

Following each passage is a variety of challenging activities. Their function is to improve students' vocabulary and reading skill—and, as enrichment, their spelling and usage, too. Here is a description of these activities:

• UNDERSTANDING WHAT YOU HAVE READ helps students to understand and enjoy the passage by asking them questions about what it states and implies. A special section early in the book teaches them how to arrive at the right answers to reading comprehension questions.

• LEARNING NEW WORDS arranges the important vocabulary of the passage for easy study and provides a clear illustrative sentence for each word taught.

• APPLYING WHAT YOU HAVE LEARNED asks students to use their new words in a variety of activities that are fun to do, including a common-sense quiz, a synonym-antonym exercise, and a picture quiz.

• LEARNING SOME DERIVATIVES trains students in forming and using derivatives, so that when they learn the word *submit*, for example, they will also be able to use *submissive*, *submissively*, and *submission*.

• IMPROVING YOUR SPELLING teaches an important spelling rule—for example, the rule for forming the plural of nouns ending in *f* or *fe*—and provides drills for mastery.

• CORRECT USAGE instructs students in a principle of usage, such as the agreement of subject and verb.

Once a word or principle has been taught, it recurs in the text. Therefore, as students progress, they will also be reviewing. In addition, a *Review* battery follows every four units, testing the vocabulary, derivatives, usage, and spelling taught in those units.

A new word does not become a part of students' vocabulary until they have used it. Therefore, they must be encouraged to use their new words in their responses in class, in compositions, and in conversations. They must be encouraged, too, to read for pleasure—hopefully, some of the works introduced in this volume—and to consult the dictionary for the meanings of unfamiliar words.

Let us now turn to the first reading selection, a passage from one of America's most famous novels, in our quest to improve VOCABULARY THROUGH PLEASURABLE READING.

H. L.

FOR YOUR READING PLEASURE

GROUP I/Reading Selections 1–4

GROUP II/Reading Selections 5–8

GROUP III/Reading Selections 9–12

GROUP IV/Reading Selections 13–16

READING SELECTION 1

On his way to school, Tom Sawyer meets Huckleberry Finn, son of the village drunkard. The respectable boys of the town have been forbidden to associate with Huck, but that makes them enjoy Huck's company all the more. Tom has a long conversation with Huck, and, as a result, he arrives at school late.

from

The Adventures of Tom Sawyer

by Mark Twain

When Tom reached the little isolated frame schoolhouse, he strode in briskly, with the manner of one who had come with all honest speed. He hung his hat on a peg and flung himself into his seat with businesslike alacrity. The master, throned on high in his great splint-bottom arm-chair, was dozing, lulled by the drowsy hum of study. The interruption roused him. 5

"Thomas Sawyer!"

Tom knew that when his name was pronounced in full, it meant trouble.

"Sir!" 10

"Come up here. Now, sir, why are you late again, as usual?"

Tom was about to take refuge in a lie, when he saw two long tails of yellow hair hanging down a back that he recognized by the electric sympathy of love; and by that form was *the only vacant place* on the girls' side of the schoolhouse. He instantly said: 15

"I STOPPED TO TALK WITH HUCKLEBERRY FINN!" The master's pulse stood still, and he stared helplessly. The buzz of study ceased. The pupils wondered if this foolhardy boy had lost his mind. The master said:

"You—you did what?" 20

"Stopped to talk with Huckleberry Finn."

There was no mistaking the words.

"Thomas Sawyer, this is the most astounding confession I have ever listened to. No mere ferule will answer for this offense.
25 Take off your jacket."

The master's arm performed until it was tired and the stock of switches notably diminished. Then the order followed:

"Now, sir, go and sit with the *girls!* And let this be a warning to you."

30 The titter that rippled around the room appeared to abash the boy, but in reality that result was caused rather more by his worshipful awe of his unknown idol and the dread pleasure that lay in his high good fortune. He sat down upon the end of the pine bench and the girl hitched herself away from him with a
35 toss of her head. Nudges and winks and whispers traversed the room, but Tom sat still, with his arms upon the long, low desk before him, and seemed to study his book.

By and by attention ceased from him, and the accustomed school murmur rose upon the dull air once more. Presently the
40 boy began to steal furtive glances at the girl. She observed it, "made a mouth" at him and gave him the back of her head for the space of a minute. When she cautiously faced around again, a peach lay before her. She thrust it away. Tom gently put it back. She thrust it away again, but with less animosity. Tom
45 patiently returned it to its place. Then she let it remain. Tom scrawled on his slate, "Please take it—I got more."

Line 4. *alacrity:* liveliness
Line 24. *ferule:* ruler used in punishing children
Line 30. *abash:* embarrass
Line 40. *furtive:* secret

Understanding What You Have Read

In the blank space, write the *letter* of the choice that best completes the statement or answers the question.

1. Tom tells the truth when asked to explain why he is late because he ____.

A. sees it is no use to lie
B. wants to make the girls feel sorry for him
C. wishes to entertain the class
D. wants to sit next to the yellow-haired girl

2. At no time in the passage does ____.

A. the master stop watching the pupils
B. Tom study his book
C. the class stop paying attention to Tom
D. the yellow-haired girl take her eyes off Tom

3. The passage suggests that ____.

2

A. Tom has often been punished by the master
B. the pupils are absolutely quiet when they study
C. except for Tom, the behavior of the class is perfect
D. Tom is usually on time

4. Of all present, who LEAST suspects Tom's true purpose in telling the truth? ____

A. the master
B. the pupils on the boys' side
C. the yellow-haired girl
D. the other girls

5. The yellow-haired girl ____.

A. pays no attention to Tom
B. shows some interest in Tom
C. hates Tom
D. asks to have her seat changed

Going Over the Answers To get the right answers to questions like the ones you were just asked, follow one simple rule: *never guess!* The proof for every right answer is in the passage. Do not put down any answer as correct unless you have found the proof for it in the passage.

Here are the correct answers to the questions you have just done. Pay attention to the reasoning used in arriving at these answers.

QUESTION 1: *Why the Correct Answer Is D:*
The "electric sympathy of love" attracts Tom to the yellow-haired girl. At the same time he notices that the only seat not taken on the girls' side is next to her. *Instantly,* he forms a plan and puts it into operation: he will *not* lie to escape punishment for being late. He will tell the truth about having been with Huck Finn because that will result in the punishment of being ordered to "go and sit with the girls." Nothing can please Tom more at this moment than the punishment of sitting next to the yellow-haired girl.

Why the Other Answers Are Wrong:
A. According to the passage, Tom is aware that lying can provide him with a *refuge,* or shelter, from punishment. Therefore, to lie might have been of some use to him.
B. Nothing in the passage shows that Tom gives any thought to the *girls.* The passage shows clearly that he is interested only in *one* girl.
C. The passage makes it clear that the reason for Tom's telling the truth is to sit near the yellow-haired girl—not to entertain the class.

QUESTION 2: *Why the Correct Answer Is B:*
Examine every reference to Tom and you will see that at no

time did he study his book. At one point he *seemed* to study his book, which means that he did *not* study.

Why the Other Answers Are Wrong:

A. The master cannot watch the class while he is *dozing*.

C. After a while, the class stops paying attention to Tom and returns to the "accustomed school murmur" of studying.

D. The yellow-haired girl took her eyes off Tom when she "gave him the back of her head for the space of a minute."

QUESTION 3: *Why the Correct Answer Is A:*

At least four statements in the passage suggest that Tom has often been punished by the master.

(1) "Tom knew that when his name was pronounced in full, it meant trouble."

(2) "Now, sir, why are you late again, as usual?"

(3) "Tom was about to take refuge in a lie" (probably, refuge from punishment by the master).

(4) "No mere ferule will answer for this offense." (This suggests that Tom has been hit with a ferule, or ruler, before for previous offenses.)

Why the Other Answers Are Wrong:

B. The passage suggests that the pupils are noisy when they study: "the drowsy hum of study" and "the accustomed school murmur."

C. The behavior of the class is not perfect. The pupils *titter*, and they exchange *nudges, winks,* and *whispers.*

D. Tom is usually late: "Now, sir, why are you late again, as usual?"

QUESTION 4: *Why the Correct Answer Is A:*

If the master had suspected Tom's true purpose, he would not have sent Tom to sit next to the yellow-haired girl.

Why the Other Answers Are Wrong:

B. and D. Tom's classmates quickly see Tom's scheme, as shown by their "nudges and winks and whispers" and "the titter that rippled around the room."

C. The yellow-haired girl knows Tom is flirting with her because she "hitched herself away from him with a toss of her head . . . 'made a mouth' at him and gave him the back of her head."

QUESTION 5: *Why the Correct Answer Is B:*

The yellow-haired girl shows interest in Tom. She watches Tom and observes that he is stealing glances at her. She gives him the back of her head, but only for "the space of a minute." She apparently will accept Tom's gift of a peach.

Why the Other Answers Are Wrong:

A. The passage shows that except for the space of a minute, when she gives Tom the back of her head, the yellow-haired girl pays complete attention to Tom.

C. It is a mistake to think that the yellow-haired girl *hates* Tom when she hitches herself away from him, or "makes a mouth," or gives him the back of her head, or at first refuses the peach. She does these things to flirt with Tom. She obviously *likes* him.

D. The yellow-haired girl does *not* ask to have her seat changed.

To sum up, to get the right answer,
1. Don't guess.
2. Find the proof for the right answer *in the passage*.
3. Check out the other answers to see why they are wrong. This will give you added proof that you have chosen the right answer.

Learning New Words

Line	Word	Meaning	Typical Use
44	**animosity** *(n.)* ˌan-ə-'mäs-ə-tē	ill will; resentment; hostility *(ant.* **good will**)	The old enemies have become friends. There is no longer any *animosity* between them.
23	**astounding** *(adj.)* ə-'staund-iŋ	filled with bewildered wonder; astonishing; amazing; surprising	When Bud, who had never pitched before, struck out the first three batters, we couldn't believe our eyes. It was an *astounding* performance.
2	**briskly** *(adv.)* 'brisk-lē	in a *brisk* (lively) manner; quickly; energetically *(ant.* **sluggishly**)	The students who are slowest in coming to class usually leave *briskly* at the bell. The mountain stream flows *sluggishly* until the rainy season, when it becomes a raging torrent.
27	**diminish** *(v.)* də-'min-ish	become or make smaller in amount, size, or importance; lessen; decrease *(ant.* **increase**)	At first my headache was unbearable, but after a while the pain *diminished*.
5	**doze** *(v.)* 'dōz	sleep lightly; be half asleep; nap	A slight noise will awake me if I am *dozing*, but not if I am sound asleep.

18	**foolhardy** *(adj.)* 'fül-ˌhärd-ē	foolishly bold; rash; reckless	To go out in sub-zero cold without a coat is *foolhardy*.
		(ant. **wary, cautious***)*	The *wary* driver locks all doors, and pockets the key before leaving his car.
			Be *cautious*. The pavement is slippery.
32	**idol** *(n.)* 'īd-əl	one that is very greatly or excessively admired or worshiped	The students worshiped the football hero; he was their *idol*.
12	**refuge** *(n.)* 'ref-yüj	shelter or protection from danger or trouble	At the height of the storm we took *refuge* in the vestibule of a building.
30	**titter** *(n.)* 'tit-ər	half-suppressed laugh; nervous laugh; giggle	The face you made when the teacher wasn't looking was responsible for a number of *titters*.
15	**vacant** *(adj.)* 'vā-kənt	having no occupant; unoccupied; empty	On the bus trip home I had to stand, as there were no *vacant* seats.

Applying What You Have Learned

I. Which of the two choices makes the sentence correct? Write the *letter* of the correct answer in the space provided.

1. The singer we are going to hear tonight is Barbara's idol. She owns ____ of his records.

A. none   B. every one

2. The apartment has been vacant since May 26, when the Browns moved ____.

A. out   B. in

3. Pete dozed in class because he ____.

A. was very excited about the lesson   B. had not had much sleep

4. After his defeat, George ____ to show that he had no animosity.

A. left abruptly   B. shook hands with his opponent

5. ____ is foolhardy.

A. Dashing across a superhighway   B. Seeking advice from others

6. It started as a titter, and quickly became a ___ laugh.

    A. half-suppressed   B. hearty

7. ___; you are walking too briskly.

    A. Try to catch up with me   B. I can't keep up with you

8. The ___ in recent months has greatly diminished our water resources.

    A. lack of rain   B. abundant rainfall

9. They offered to ___ home, but we were not in need of refuge.

    A. take us into their   B. come to our

10. The news that I was to receive the math prize was astounding because I had never thought I ___.

    A. had a chance to win   B. was inferior to any of the other math students

II. The meaning of each expression can be found in the vocabulary list at the bottom of the exercise. Find that meaning and write it in the space provided.

_____ 1. in a lively manner

_____ 2. person excessively admired

_____ 3. sleep lightly

_____ 4. ill will

_____ 5. having no occupant

_____ 6. foolishly bold

_____ 7. become smaller in amount

_____ 8. nervous laugh

_____ 9. filled with bewildered wonder

_____ 10. shelter from danger

Vocabulary List

doze	vacant
diminish	briskly
idol	refuge
astounding	animosity
foolhardy	titter

III. Synonyms and Antonyms

Fill the blanks in column A with the required synonyms or antonyms, selecting them from column B.

	Column A	*Column B*
_____	1. synonym for *unoccupied*	foolhardy
_____	2. synonym for *surprising*	animosity
_____	3. antonym for *wary*	titter
_____	4. synonym for *shelter*	astounding
_____	5. synonym for *nap*	idol
_____	6. antonym for *good will*	doze
_____	7. antonym for *increase*	briskly
_____	8. antonym for *sluggishly*	vacant
_____	9. synonym for *giggle*	diminish
_____	10. synonym for *worshiped person*	refuge

IV. Picture Quiz

In the blank space, write the *letter* of the picture that best fits the meaning of the sentence.

1. ____ is not foolhardy.

8

2. ＿＿＿ usually moves at a brisk pace.

3. ＿＿＿ seems to be dozing.

Learning Some Derivatives

Suppose you have just learned that the adjective *vacant* means "unoccupied." Now, if you were to see the noun *vacancy* in a sign outside an apartment building, you could easily tell that it means an "unoccupied apartment." Also, if you were to come across the verb *vacate* (the residents were ordered to *vacate* the building), you would know that it means to "go away from," or "leave unoccupied."

A word like *vacancy* or *vacate* is called a *derivative* because it is derived (formed) from another word—the word *vacant*.

A word like *vacant* from which other words are derived is called a *root*.

Each word in bold type below is a *root*. The words below it are its *derivatives*.

brisk *(adj.)* — Because of the heat the refreshment stand did a *brisk* business.

briskly *(adv.)* — Cold soda sold *briskly*.

briskness *(n.)* — The owner was obviously pleased with the *briskness* of soda sales.

doze *(v.)* — If you *doze* at your desk, it may be that you have not had enough sleep.

doze *(n.)* — A brief *doze* can be very refreshing.

dozer *(n.)* — Our conversation did not seem to disturb the *dozer* at the other end of the park bench.

foolhardy *(adj.)* — Since Tom is a poor swimmer, it was *foolhardy* for him to try to swim to the raft.

foolhardiness *(n.)* — As a result of his *foolhardiness,* Tom might have drowned.

idol *(n.)* — Which sports star, actor, or singer is your *idol*?

idolize *(v.)* — Which sports star, actor, or singer do you *idolize*?

refuge *(n.)* — People made homeless by the hurricane were given *refuge* in public buildings.

refugee *(n.)* — *Refugees* from the hurricane were given shelter in public buildings.

titter *(v.)* — Charley's comic expression made me *titter*.

titter *(n.)* — When Charley made a face, I could not suppress a *titter*.

vacate *(v.)* — Please notify us if some guests should *vacate* their rooms.

vacant *(adj.)* — Please notify us as soon as a room becomes *vacant*.

vacancy *(n.)* — Please notify us when there is a *vacancy*.

Fill each blank below with the word listed previously that best fits the meaning of the sentence.

1. The ringing of the telephone awakened me from my _____.

2. A "no _____" sign outside the motel indicated that every room was taken.

3. Working with remarkable _____, the movers unloaded the van in much less time than I had thought it would take.

10

4. The _____, who has been given protection in our country, hopes to return to his native land once democracy is restored there.

5. We spoke in whispers for fear of awakening the weary _____.

6. The child cannot keep up with you if you walk at too _____ a pace.

7. The student telling the joke began to _____ long before the rest of the class saw anything to laugh at.

8. If you succeed you will become a hero, and people will _____ you.

9. The reckless lad has just committed another act of _____.

10. During a fire drill, all students and teachers must _____ the building.

Improving Your Spelling: Consonants Often Omitted

"Tom . . . saw two long tails of yellow hair hanging down a back that he recognized . . ."

One of the most difficult words to spell in the above quotation is *recognized.* Many students carelessly omit the *g* when they say the word.

The words below are similar to *recognized:* they each contain a consonant that is often carelessly omitted when the word is said or written. The troublesome consonant is highlighted; be sure to include it in your pronunciation and also in your spelling.

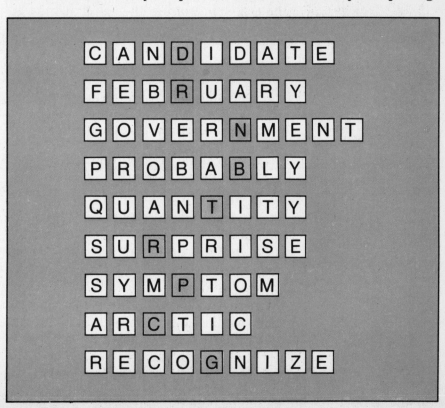

CANDIDATE
FEBRUARY
GOVERNMENT
PROBABLY
QUANTITY
SURPRISE
SYMPTOM
ARCTIC
RECOGNIZE

Study the words just listed. When you feel you know how to spell them, do the exercises that follow.

I. Fill in the missing letters in column A, and write the complete word in column B.

Column A | Column B

1. s ___ ___ prise _____

2. lib ___ ___ ry _____

3. can ___ ___ date _____

4. Feb ___ ___ ary _____

5. sy ___ ___ tom _____

6. rec ___ ___ nize _____

7. gov ___ ___ ___ ment _____

8. prob ___ ___ ly _____

9. repres ___ ___ ___ ___ tive _____

10. quan ___ ___ ty _____

II. Fill in the missing letters of each incomplete word. Then write the complete word in the space at the left.

_____ 1. Large quan ___ ___ t ___ ___ s of supplies are being delivered.

_____ 2. The lib ___ ___ rian showed me how to use the card catalog.

_____ 3. How many members are there in the House of ___ epresen ___ ___ tives?

_____ 4. The robbers wore masks to prevent rec ___ ___ nition.

_____ 5. S ___ ___ prisingly, the horse that was supposed to come in last won the race.

_____ 6. Feb ___ ___ ___ ___ y 14 is Saint Valentine's Day.

_____ 7. As you know, the FBI is a gover ___ ___ ental agency.

_____ 8. You are prob ___ ___ ___ y right.

_____ 9. After an hour, the hikers began to show sy ___ ___ t ___ ms of weariness.

_____ 10. The submarine sailed north into the A ___ ___ tic Ocean.

Correct Usage: Distinguishing Between *It's* and *Its*

1. As we have previously learned, *it's* is a contraction meaning "it is."

> *a.* It's two o'clock.
>
> *b.* Jeff says it's raining.

2. On the other hand, *its* (no apostrophe) is a possessive meaning "belonging to it."

> *c.* The river overflowed its banks.
>
> *d.* The cat hurt its paw.

Insert *it's* or *its* as required by the sentence. *Hint:* If "it is" can replace *it's* and make sense, you can be sure *it's* is correct. Otherwise, use *its*.

1. Our team is proud of _____ record.

2. Don't remove the cake from the oven until _____ done.

3. _____ too bad you were not present.

4. You can't judge a book by _____ cover.

5. Sheila will take good care of the guitar because she knows _____ value.

6. Sometimes a dog disobeys _____ master.

7. Be careful with that knife; _____ very sharp.

8. Don't you think _____ time to go?

9. _____ not your fault.

10. The tornado destroyed everything in _____ path.

It is 1873, and you have just completed your freshman year in college. Everyone is returning home for the summer vacation—everyone except you. You can't go home because you have no money. What are you to do?

from

Up From Slavery

by Booker T. Washington

AT THE END of my first year at Hampton I was confronted with another difficulty. Most of the students went home to spend their vacation. I had no money with which to go home, but I had to go somewhere. In those days very few students were permitted to
5 remain at the school during vacation. It made me feel very sad and homesick to see the other students preparing to leave and starting for home. I not only had no money with which to go home, but I had none with which to go anywhere.

In some way, however, I had gotten hold of an extra, second-
10 hand coat which I thought was a pretty valuable coat. This I decided to sell, in order to get a little money for travelling expenses. I had a good deal of boyish pride, and I tried to hide, as far as I could, from the other students the fact that I had no money and nowhere to go. I made it known to a few people in the town of
15 Hampton that I had this coat to sell, and, after a good deal of persuading, one coloured man promised to come to my room to look the coat over and consider the matter of buying it. This cheered my drooping spirits considerably. Early the next morning my prospective customer appeared. After looking the garment over
20 carefully, he asked me how much I wanted for it. I told him I thought it was worth three dollars. He seemed to agree with me as to price, but remarked in the most matter-of-fact way: "I tell you what I will do; I will take the coat, and I will pay you five

cents, cash down, and pay you the rest of the money just as soon
as I can get it." It is not hard to imagine what my feelings were   25
at the time.

With this disappointment I gave up all hope of getting out of
the town of Hampton for my vacation work. I wanted very much
to go where I might secure work that would at least pay me enough
to purchase some much-needed clothing and other necessities.   30
In a few days practically all the students and teachers had left
for their homes, and this served to depress my spirits even more.

Understanding What You Have Read

In the blank space, write the *letter* of the choice that best completes the statement.

1. Booker T. Washington ____ .

   A. has more than one problem
   B. does not need clothes
   C. is the only student who did not go home for the vacation
   D. does not have a home to return to

2. Booker is inclined to ____ .

   A. seek help from his fellow students
   B. blame others for his misfortune
   C. keep his troubles to himself
   D. complain to others about his hard luck

3. The passage ____ .

   A. describes how Booker acquired the second-hand coat
   B. indicates that he sold the second-hand coat
   C. fails to indicate whether he sold the second-hand coat or not
   D. indicates that he did not sell the second-hand coat

4. As far as money is concerned, Booker seems to be in about the same situation as ____ .

   A. the customer for the second-hand coat
   B. most of the other students
   C. the teachers
   D. the people in the town of Hampton

5. There is no evidence in the passage that Booker is ____ .

   A. homesick
   B. willing to work
   C. lonely
   D. getting poor grades

Learning New Words

Line	Word	Meaning	Typical Use
1	**confront** (v.) kən-'frənt	face, especially in challenge; meet face to face; oppose	Tonight, the Mets oppose the Phils; tomorrow they *confront* the Giants.
18	**considerably** (adv.) kən-'sid-ər-əb-lē	greatly; much; to a large extent	There was hardly a scratch on our car, but the other vehicle was *considerably* damaged.
32	**depress** (v.) di-'pres	sadden; discourage; make gloomy (ant. **cheer**)	When you visit a patient, try to cheer him up. Don't say anything that might *depress* him.
18	**drooping** (adj.) 'drüp-iŋ	hanging down; losing strength; becoming weak	After the storm, when the sun came out, the *drooping* flowers began to raise their heads.
19	**garment** (n.) 'gär-mənt	article of clothing	Mother saves Dad's old *garments* so that he may wear them when he does messy jobs.
22	**matter-of-fact** (adj.) ˌmat-ər-ə-'fakt	sticking strictly to facts; unimaginative; concerned with the obvious and overlooking the deeper reality (ant. **imaginative**)	The teacher showed me that my descriptions are too *matter-of-fact*; they lack imagination. A news story must stick to the facts; it should not be *imaginative*.
30	**necessity** (n.) ni-'ses-ə-tē	very necessary thing; something that cannot be done without; need	Food, shelter, and clothing are *necessities*—everyone must have them.
31	**practically** (adv.) 'prak-ti-kə-lē	almost; very nearly	Mother is going shopping, since there is *practically* no food left in the refrigerator.
12	**pride** (n.) 'prīd	1. self-respect; sense of one's own worth or dignity	Sam has too much self-respect to back out. To be called a quitter would be a blow to his *pride*.

16

2. delight or satisfaction in one's achievements or possessions

(*ant.* **shame**)

Grandma was pleased when I praised her pancakes. She takes *pride* in her cooking.

19 **prospective**
   (adj.)
   prə-'spek-tiv

likely to be or become; expected; probable

My brother introduced his *prospective* bride; they are to be married in June.

Applying What You Have Learned

I. Which of the two choices makes the sentence correct? Write the *letter* of the correct answer in the space provided.

1. ____ are not necessities.

   A. Jewelry and sports cars   B. Clean air and water

2. The news of your ____ depressed us.

   A. unfortunate accident   B. safe arrival

3. We are looking ____ our prospective vacation.

   A. back on   B. forward to

4. A ____ is not a garment.

   A. curtain   B. bathrobe

5. We returned to the field with the drooping spirits of a team that was sure to ____.

   A. win   B. lose

6. The new student arrived in ____, when the school year was practically over.

   A. May   B. November

7. Under our system of justice, a defendant has the right of confronting his ____.

   A. accusers   B. friends

8. Do you prefer a matter-of-fact news commentator, or one who ____?

   A. does not omit important details   B. looks into the deeper reality of things

9. When a student needs a scolding, Mrs. Kapp will give it to him in ____ to reduce the blow to his pride.

   A. front of the whole class   B. private

10. My brother is 21 and my sister is considerably younger; she is ____.

    A. 14   B. 18

II. The meaning of each expression below can be found in the vocabulary list at the bottom of the exercise. Find that meaning and write it in the space provided.

_____ 1. sense of one's own worth

_____ 2. article of clothing

_____ 3. likely to be or become

_____ 4. hanging down

_____ 5. to a large extent

_____ 6. make gloomy

_____ 7. meet face to face

_____ 8. sticking strictly to facts

_____ 9. very nearly

_____ 10. something that we cannot do without

Vocabulary List

considerably	prospective
necessity	practically
pride	garment
depress	drooping
confront	matter-of-fact

III. Fill the blanks with the required synonyms or antonyms, selecting them from the vocabulary list on the next page.

1. synonym for _almost:_ _____

2. antonym for _imaginative:_ _____

3. synonym for _clothing:_ _____

4. synonym for _oppose:_ _____

5. antonym for _shame:_ _____

6. synonym for _need:_ _____

7. synonym for _greatly:_ _____

8. antonym for _cheer:_ _____

9. synonym for _expected:_ _____

10. synonym for _weakening:_ _____

Vocabulary List

garments	matter-of-fact
depress	considerably
pride	confront
prospective	drooping
practically	necessity

IV. Picture Quiz

In the blank space, write the *letter* of the picture that best fits the meaning of the sentence.

1. _____ is a prospective college graduate.

2. Banner _____ is drooping.

3. _____ is not a garment.

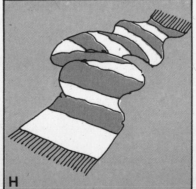

Learning Some Derivatives

Each word in bold type below is a *root*. The words below it are its *derivatives*.

confront *(v.)*   My opponent has refused to take part in a debate because he is afraid to *confront* me.

confrontation *(n.)*   My opponent is seeking to avoid a *confrontation* with me.

considerable *(adj.)*   You have shown *considerable* improvement.

considerably *(adv.)*   You have improved *considerably*.

depress *(v.)*   Do low grades *depress* you?

depressing *(adj.)*   To me, a low grade is *depressing*.

depressingly *(adv.)*   My first mark in French was *depressingly* low.

depression *(n.)*   It threw me into a fit of *depression*.

droop *(v.)*   Plants may *droop* from a lack of moisture.

drooping *(adj.)*   Rain gives *drooping* plants a new lease on life.

droopingly *(adv.)*   Thirsty plants bow their heads *droopingly*.

matter-of-fact *(adj.)*   The reporter wrote a *matter-of-fact* account of the event.

matter-of-factly *(adv.)*   He reported the event *matter-of-factly*.

matter-of-factness *(n.)*   He described the event with *matter-of-factness*.

necessity *(n.)*   Is a bicycle a *necessity* for the job?

necessary *(adj.)*   Will a bicycle be *necessary*?

necessarily *(adv.)*   Do you *necessarily* have to have a bicycle?

necessitate *(v.)*   Does the job *necessitate* that you have a bicycle?

prospect *(n.)*   The *prospect* of a snowfall appealed to the children.

prospective *(adj.)*   The children were happy about the *prospective* snowfall.

proud *(adj.)*   We are *proud* of our work.

proudly *(adv.)*   We talk *proudly* of our work.

pride *(n.)*   We speak of our work with *pride*.

pride *(v.)*   We *pride* ourselves on our work.

Fill each blank with the word just listed that best fits the meaning of the sentence.

1. You cannot learn a foreign language overnight. It takes a _____ amount of time and study.

2. The banners that had fluttered so gayly began to _____ in the dying breeze.

3. Our record this year of eight defeats and no victories is very _____. Most of the team is discouraged.

4. The opposing candidates have agreed to debate the issues face to face. Their first _____ will be on Channel 6 tomorrow at 10 P.M.

5. Here are two very urgent problems that _____ our immediate attention.

6. There is a strong likelihood that Stan will make a complete recovery, but there is little _____ that he will be able to play in any of the remaining games this season.

7. Poets write imaginatively, not _____.

8. Maureen, who is usually very cheerful, is in a state of _____ because she has not been invited to Alison's party.

9. Take along only what is _____ for the trip. Do not burden yourself with things you can do without.

10. My sister takes delight in her achievements as an honor pupil, while I _____ myself on being a good athlete.

Improving Your Spelling: Compound Words

A *compound word* is formed from two or more words joined together.

Note that a compound word usually *keeps all the letters of the words from which it is formed*.

```
CLASS + [MATE] = CLASS [MATE]
 TEAM + [MATE] =  TEAM [MATE]
 ROOM + [MATE] =  ROOM [MATE]

[SOME] +  ONE  = [SOME] ONE
[SOME] + THING = [SOME] THING
[SOME] + TIME  = [SOME] TIME
```

I. Form three compound words with each italicized word. Study the two examples that follow.

door + man = **doorman**	*color* + *less* = **colorless**
+ way = **doorway**	odor + = **odorless**
+ knob = **doorknob**	taste + = **tasteless**

1. *some* + body = _____
   + one = _____
   + where = _____

2. book + *keeper* = _____
   house + = _____
   store + = _____

3. *home* + made = _____
   + less = _____
   + work = _____

4. class + *mate* = _____
   team + = _____
   room + = _____

5. *no* + where = _____
   + body = _____
   + thing = _____

6. sea + *sick* = _____
   heart + = _____
   home + = _____

7. *every* + one = _____
   + thing = _____
   + where = _____

8. head + *ache* = _____
   back + = _____
   tooth + = _____

9. *any* + where = _____
   + one = _____
   + body = _____

10. sales + *man* = _____
    service + = _____
    business + = _____

II. Write the compound word.

SAMPLE: here + after = **hereafter**

1. never + the + less = _____

2. here + by = _____

3. dumb + bell = _____

4. extra + ordinary = _____

22

5. hair + do = _____

6. in + as + much = _____

7. up + keep = _____

8. hand + kerchief = _____

9. here + to + fore = _____

10. make + up = _____

III. One word in each line is misspelled. Spell that word correctly in the space at the right.

1. timekeeper, somwhere, everyone _____

2. homemade, saleslady, roomate _____

3. doornob, passageway, gentleman _____

4. painless, hankerchief, toothache _____

5. anyone, nowhere, somone _____

6. salesgirl, bookeeper, hereafter _____

7. teamate, seasick, heartless _____

8. penmanship, businesman, shoeless _____

9. housekeeper, everyone, dumbell _____

10. heretofore, extrordinary, mailman _____

Correct Usage: Avoiding Double Negatives

QUESTION: He did not have _____ money. (*no* or *any*?)

ANSWER: He did not have *any* money.

EXPLANATION: In making a negative statement, we use only one negative word. Since the sentence already contains one negative word, *not*, it would be a mistake to choose *no*, which is also a negative word. Therefore *any* is the correct answer.

ALSO CORRECT: He had *no* money.

EXPLANATION: In this case *no* may be used, since the sentence contains no other negative word.

The following are some common negative words. Be careful to use only one of them in each negative statement:

no	never	no one	neither	scarcely
not	nobody	none	barely	only
-n't	nowhere	nothing	hardly	but (meaning *only*)

One negative word is identified in each sentence below to warn you that you may not use another negative word in that sentence. Write the correct answer in the blank.

1. I did n't have _____ to do with it.
(anything, nothing)

2. Sam has hardly _____ friends.
(any, no)

3. Try to catch some worms; we could n't find _____.
(none, any)

4. Where are Joe and Bill? I have not seen _____ of them today.
(either, neither)

5. Our teacher did n't fail _____ in that test.
(nobody, anybody)

6. You did it yourself. You do n't have _____ else to blame.
(no one, anyone)

7. Jim's brother _____ barely five feet tall.
(is, isn't)

8. Most of us have n't _____ gone camping.
(never, ever)

9. I _____ but two sheets of paper left.
(have, haven't)

10. She told us that she _____ nothing to do with Laura.
(didn't have, had)

II. Below, on line A, is one correct way of making a negative statement. On line B, make the same statement in another equally correct way. Note these samples:

A. I don't have any time.
B. **I have no time.**

A. We found nobody at home.
B. **We didn't find anybody at home.**

1. A. You have not answered any of my questions.

B. _____

2. A. We are not getting anywhere.

B. _____

3. A. There are no napkins left.

    B. _____

4. A. I didn't care for either of them.

    B. _____

5. A. She had never been to the zoo.

    B. _____

6. A. They didn't have anybody to help them.

    B. _____

7. A. He has nothing to complain about.

    B. _____

8. A. I looked for errors but I found none.

    B. _____

9. A. Don't mention it to anyone.

    B. _____

10. A. There aren't any signs of improvement.

    B. _____

Jody Baxter, his father Penny, and their dogs Julia and Rip close in on Old Slewfoot, the huge black outlaw bear who has destroyed some of the Baxter livestock. Suddenly, Julia barks and Penny runs ahead, shouting.

from

The Yearling

by Marjorie Kinnan Rawlings

"The Creek!" he shouted. "He's tryin' to make the Creek!"

Sound filled the swamp. Saplings crashed. The bear was a black hurricane, mowing down obstructions. The dogs barked and bayed. The roaring in Jody's ears was his heart pounding. A bamboo vine tripped him and he sprawled and was on his feet again. Penny's short legs churned in front of him like paddles. Slewfoot would make Juniper Creek before the dogs could halt him at bay.

A clear space opened at the creek's bank. Jody saw a vast black shapeless form break through. Penny halted and lifted his gun. On the instant, a small brown missile hurled itself at the shaggy head. Old Julia had caught up with her enemy. She leaped and retreated, and in the moment of retreat, was at him again. Rip darted in beside her. Slewfoot wheeled and slashed at him. Julia flashed at his flank. Penny held his fire. He could not shoot, for the dogs.

Old Slewfoot was suddenly, deceptively, indifferent. He seemed to stand baffled, slow and uncertain, weaving back and forth. He whined, like a child whimpering. The dogs backed off an instant. The moment was perfect for a shot and Penny swung his gun to his shoulder, drew a bead on the left cheek, and pulled the trigger. A harmless pop sounded. He cocked the hammer again and pulled the trigger once more. The sweat stood out on his forehead. Again

the hammer clicked futilely. Then a black storm broke. It roared
in on the dogs with incredible swiftness. White tusks and curved   25
claws were streaks of lightning across it. It snarled and whirled
and gnashed its teeth and slashed in every direction. The dogs
were as quick. Julia made swift sorties from the rear, and when
Slewfoot wheeled to rake at her, Rip leaped for the hairy throat.

Jody was in a paralysis of horror. He saw that his father had   30
cocked the hammer again and stood half-crouching, licking his
lips, fingering the trigger. Old Julia bored in at the bear's right
flank. He wheeled, not on her, but on the bulldog at his left. He
caught him sideways and sent him sprawling into the bushes.
Again Penny pulled the trigger. The explosion that followed had   35
a sizzling sound, and Penny fell backward. The gun had back-fired.

Rip returned to his attempts for the bear's throat and Julia
took up her worrying from the rear. The bear stood again at bay,
weaving. Jody ran to his father. Penny was already on his feet.
The right side of his face was black with powder. Slewfoot shook   40
free of Rip, whirled to Julia and caught her to his chest with his
cupped claws. She yelped sharply. Rip hurled himself at the back
and buried his teeth in the hide.

Jody screamed, "He's killin' Julia!"

Penny ran desperately into the heart of the fracas. He jammed   45
the gun barrel in the bear's ribs. Even in her pain, Julia had taken
a grip on the black throat above her. Slewfoot snarled and turned
suddenly and plunged down the bank of the creek and into the
deep water. Both dogs kept their hold. Slewfoot swam madly.
Only Julia's head showed above water, below the bear's snout.   50
Rip rode the broad back with bravado. Slewfoot made the far bank
and scrambled up its side. Julia loosed her hold and dropped limply
on the earth. The bear plunged toward the dense thicket. For a
moment more Rip stayed with him. Then, confused, he too dropped
away and turned back uncertainly to the creek. He snuffed at   55
Julia and sat down on his haunches and howled across the water.
There was a crashing in the distant undergrowth, then silence.

Line 4. *bayed:* howled
Line 8. *at bay:* with escape cut off
Line 28. *sorties:* attacks
Line 29. *rake:* scratch
Line 30. *paralysis:* loss of ability to act
Line 45. *fracas:* noisy fight
Line 51. *bravado:* show of bravery

Understanding What You Have Read

In the blank space, write the *letter* of the choice that best completes the statement.

1. During the battle with Slewfoot, Jody ＿＿.

   A. pokes him in the ribs

B. pulls Old Julia to safety
C. screams
D. remains calm

2. In their attack on the bear, _____.

A. Old Julia leads and Rip follows
B. Rip leads and Old Julia follows
C. the dogs do not work together as a team
D. the dogs give Penny no chance for a shot

3. When a gun barrel is jammed into his ribs, Slewfoot _____.

A. yelps in pain
B. plunges into the creek
C. shakes himself free of the dogs
D. stands baffled

4. The most seriously injured in this fierce encounter was _____.

A. Penny
B. Old Slewfoot
C. Rip
D. Old Julia

5. The bear escapes mainly because of _____.

A. his cleverness
B. Penny's poor marksmanship
C. the dogs' cowardice
D. equipment failure

Learning New Words

Line	Word	Meaning	Typical Use
18	**baffle** (*v.*) 'baf-əl	confuse, so as to keep from understanding; puzzle; perplex	At first I didn't recognize you. Your clever disguise *baffled* me.
17	**deceptively** (*adv.*) di-'sep-tiv-lē	in a *deceptive* (misleading) way; trickily	As the victim walked into the ambush, all was *deceptively* quiet and peaceful.
		(*ant.* **genuinely**)	When I asked for permission to go home, I was *genuinely* ill. I was not pretending.

53	**dense** *(adj.)* 'dens	1. packed tightly together; compact; thick	The thief escaped capture by mingling with the *dense* crowd.
		(*ant.* **sparse**)	An overflow crowd had been expected, but the turnout was *sparse*.
		2. mentally dull; slow to understand; stupid	Three of my friends have explained the first problem to me, but I still don't understand it. I fear I am becoming *dense*.
		(*ant.* **bright, intelligent**)	
15	**flank** *(n.)* 'flaŋk	fleshy side between the ribs and the hip; right or left side of a formation; side	The cow kept swishing her tail to chase the flies from her *flank*.
24	**futilely** *(adv.)* 'fyü-ˌtəl-ē	in a *futile* (vain) manner; vainly; uselessly	My sister raised her fist *futilely* at the waves that were knocking her down.
		(*ant.* **effectively**)	We tried to stop the leak without success; however, the plumber dealt with it *effectively*.
25	**incredible** *(adj.)* in-'kred-ə-bəl	too extraordinary to be believed; hard to believe; unbelievable	Light travels at the *incredible* speed of 186,000 miles a second.
		(*ant.* **believable, credible**)	When a report comes from a *credible* source, we are inclined to accept it without question.
17	**indifferent** *(adj.)* in-'dif-rənt	showing no concern, interest, or feeling; uninterested; unconcerned	Most students are concerned about whether they will pass or fail, but Ed seems *indifferent*.
		(*ant.* **eager**)	
11	**missile** *(n.)* 'mis-əl	weapon or object thrown at a target; projectile	In her anger, Mary threw a shoe at me because it was the nearest thing she could use as a *missile*.
3	**obstruction** *(n.)* əb-'strək-shən	something that *obstructs* or is in the way; hindrance; obstacle	A disabled vehicle in the middle of a road is an *obstruction* to traffic.
12	**shaggy** *(adj.)* 'shag-ē	covered with a thick, rough mass of hair; hairy	Dad took the twins to the barber because they were beginning to look *shaggy*.

Applying What You Have Learned

I. Which of the two choices makes the sentence correct? Write the *letter* of the correct answer in the space provided.

1. A ____ can easily be used as a missile.

   A. stone   B. highway

2. With opponents swiftly closing in on the flanks, I had nowhere to run but ____.

   A. to the right   B. straight ahead

3. Shaggy dogs have ____ coats of fur.

   A. thick   B. thin

4. It is not easy to ____ in the dense woods.

   A. hide   B. see ahead

5. Joe's explanation was incredible; ____ believed it.

   A. no one   B. everyone

6. The bundle was deceptively heavy; it seemed to be ____ to lift.

   A. hard   B. easy

7. The youngster screamed futilely; ____.

   A. his parents came running   B. no one paid attention

8. An indifferent person has ____ for those who suffer.

   A. no concern   B. great pity

9. The crossword puzzle in the school newspaper baffled me. I ____.

   A. did it in about a quarter of an hour   B. haven't been able to finish it

10. An obstruction ____.

   A. blocks passage   B. prevents delay

II. The meaning of each expression below can be found in the vocabulary list at the bottom of the exercise. Find that meaning and write it in the space provided.

_____ **1.** too extraordinary to be believed

_____ **2.** packed tightly together

_____ **3.** something in the way

_____ **4.** showing no concern

_____ 5. in a misleading way

_____ 6. weapon thrown at a target

_____ 7. covered with a mass of hair

_____ 8. fleshy side between ribs and hip

_____ 9. in a vain manner

_____ 10. confuse, so as to keep from understanding

Vocabulary List

flank	deceptively
baffle	obstruction
indifferent	incredible
shaggy	missile
dense	futilely

III. Synonyms and Antonyms

A. Replace the italicized word with a *synonym* from the vocabulary list on the next page.

_____ 1. The parade proceeded in an orderly manner with mounted policemen on each *side* of the marchers.

_____ 2. A *projectile* was thrown by someone in the crowd, but it landed harmlessly.

_____ 3. My brother's heavy dark beard and sideburns give him a *hairy* appearance.

_____ 4. Vague language is a serious *hindrance* to communication.

_____ 5. These directions are very clear and should not *perplex* anybody.

B. Replace each italicized word with an *antonym* from the vocabulary list.

_____   **6.** The goods were on sale at *genuinely* reduced prices.

_____   **7.** The report seemed entirely *believable*.

_____   **8.** Because of the weather, the crowds at the beaches were *sparse*.

_____   **9.** When I spoke to Nina about joining our club, she seemed *eager*.

_____   **10.** Some housewives have protested *effectively* against higher food costs.

Vocabulary List

shaggy	indifferent
incredible	flank
futilely	baffle
missile	dense
deceptively	obstruction

IV. Picture Quiz

In the blank space, write the *letter* of the picture that best fits the meaning of the sentence.

1. ____ is a shaggy creature.

2. ____ is doing something futile.

3. The most densely populated area is ____.

Learning Some Derivatives

Each word in bold type below is a *root*. The words below it are its *derivatives*.

baffle *(v.)*	How do you solve that problem? It *baffles* me.
baffling *(adj.)*	I find that problem very *baffling*.
deceive *(v.)*	Do you think I will *deceive* you?
deceptive *(adj.)*	I am not *deceptive*. I tell the truth.
deceptively *(adv.)*	I do not behave *deceptively*.
deception *(n.)*	I do not practice *deception*.
deceiver *(n.)*	I am no *deceiver*.
dense *(adj.)*	Some cities have a *dense* population.
densely *(adv.)*	Farm areas are not *densely* populated.

density *(n.)*	Farm areas have a low population *density*.
flank *(n.)*	Our ball-carrier needs protection on his right *flank*.
flank *(v.)*	I will *flank* him on the right if you will protect him on the left side.
futile *(adj.)*	Our opponents were too husky. It was *futile* to try to stop them.
futilely *(adv.)*	We tried *futilely* to stop our opponents; they kept scoring.
futility *(n.)*	Despite the *futility* of our efforts, we kept trying.
incredible *(adj.)*	Larry saved the game with an *incredible* catch.
incredibly *(adv.)*	He made an *incredibly* difficult catch against the right-field wall.
incredibility *(n.)*	We are still marveling at the *incredibility* of that catch.
indifferent *(adj.)*	I went to their assistance because I could not remain *indifferent;* they needed help.
indifferently *(adv.)*	When I saw they were in trouble, I could not pass by *indifferently*.
indifference *(n.)*	The two dazed occupants were standing beside their wrecked car. I could not look on with *indifference*.
obstruct *(v.)*	Sometimes legislators try to *obstruct* the passage of a bill.
obstructive *(adj.)*	They hold up passage of the bill by means of long *obstructive* speeches. Such speeches are called a filibuster.
obstruction *(n.)*	A filibuster is an *obstruction* to the passage of legislation.

I. Fill each blank below with the word listed previously that best fits the meaning of the sentence.

1. We have laws that are designed to protect us from being misled by _____ advertising.

2. When the surrounded burglar realized that it was _____ to resist, he surrendered to the police.

3. As night fell, the _____ of the fog increased.

4. If you put hindrances in our path, you are being _____.

5. It was a(an) _____ case, but Sherlock Holmes solved it.

6. Our farm areas are now sparsely inhabited, while our cities are becoming more _____ populated.

7. Myths, fairy tales, and legends appeal to us in spite of their _____.

8. Marty has a strange attitude of _____ to the examination: he doesn't care whether he passes or fails.

9. You can depend on Joe to tell the truth; he will not _____ you.

10. The disabled truck was towed off the bridge because it was a(an) _____ to traffic.

II. Next to each word or expression below, write the word listed previously that most nearly has the same meaning.

1. in an unconcerned manner   _____

2. ineffectiveness   _____

3. unbelievably   _____

4. be at the side of   _____

5. trickily   _____

6. perplex   _____

7. one who misleads   _____

8. stupid   _____

9. hinder   _____

10. trickery   _____

Improving Your Spelling: Silent Letters

The black bear "snarled and whirled and *gnashed* its teeth . . ."

Notice that the g in *gnashed* is not pronounced. It is a silent letter, like the t in *listen,* or the k in *knee.*

Say each of the following words aloud, leaving out the silent letters. Remember, however, to *put the silent letters in when you write these words:*

SILENT *b*	SILENT *c*	SILENT *d*
bom*b*	des*c*end	han*d*kerchief
clim*b*	fas*c*inate	a*d*jective
com*b*	mus*c*le	a*d*join
crum*b*	s*c*issors	a*d*just
de*b*t	a*c*quire	(and all other
dou*b*t	a*c*quaint	*adj* words)
dum*b*	(and all other	
plum*b*er	*acq* words)	

SILENT *g*	SILENT *h*	SILENT *k*
desi*g*n	ex*h*aust	ac*k*nowledge
*g*nash	ex*h*ibit	*k*nack
*g*naw	*g*host	*k*nee
*g*nome	*h*eir	*k*nob
si*g*n	*h*erb	(and all other
	she*ph*erd	*k*n words)
	ve*h*icle	

SILENT *l*	SILENT *n*	SILENT *p*
a*l*mond	autum*n*	em*p*ty
ca*l*m	colum*n*	*p*neumonia
fo*l*k	condem*n*	*p*sychology
pa*l*m	hym*n*	recei*p*t
sa*l*mon		
yo*l*k		

SILENT *s*	SILENT *t*	SILENT *w*
ai*s*le	bankrup*t*cy	ans*w*er
i*s*land	Chris*t*mas	play*w*right
i*s*le	lis*t*en	s*w*ord
	mor*t*gage	*w*hole
	sof*t*en	*w*rap
	wres*t*le (the *w* is	(and all other
	silent, too)	*wr* words)

I. One word in each line below is misspelled; write that word correctly in the blank space.

_____ **1.** unknown, climber, ajoin, plumber

_____ **2.** adjusted, exausted, folk, descended

_____ **3.** almond, fasinating, doubtful, bombshell

_____ **4.** hym, wrestler, salmon, acknowledge

_____ **5.** whole, knee, condem, isle

_____ **6.** ghost, herb, knack, aquired

_____ **7.** scissors, crumb, receit, bankruptcy

_____ **8.** aquainted, dumb, knuckle, Christmas

_____ **9.** yolk, neumonia, writer, column

_____ **10.** playright, palm, muscle, shepherd

_____ **11.** almond, wrist, anser, knee

_____ **12.** calm, neebending, indebted, island

_____ 13. lissen, designer, bomb, heir

_____ 14. wrapping, exibition, knock, plumbing

_____ 15. combed, soften, morgage, vehicle

_____ 16. sword, adjoining, autumn, hankerchief

_____ 17. sychological, gnashed, doubtless, acquaintance

_____ 18. debtor, emty-handed, adjustment, dumbfounded

_____ 19. doornob, fascination, typewriter, folklore

_____ 20. aisle, column, adjacent, holeheartedly

II. One word in each sentence below has been omitted, but its pronunciation is given. You can tell the number of letters in the missing word by the number of spaces provided at the right. Study the following sample. Then fill in the other missing words.

I am in ['det] to my brother because I still owe him two
dollars. **d e b t**

1. Why don't you ['an-sər] her question? — — — — — —

2. It is impolite to ['kōm] your hair in public. — — — —

3. Do you prefer spring or ['ȯt-əm]? — — — — — —

4. A bicycle is a two-wheeled ['vē-ˌik-əl]. — — — — — — —

5. What do you have in the ['päm] óf your hand? — — — —

6. Please keep your feet under your desk; do not put them out

   in the ['īl]. — — — — —

7. In the phrase "a wonderful time," "wonderful" is an

   ['aj-ik-tiv]. — — — — — — — — —

8. Mother uses aluminum foil to ['rap] my sandwiches. — — — —

9. I tried my best, but I could not untie the ['nät]. — — — —

10. The car would not start because the gas tank was ['em-tē]. — — — — —

Grammar: The Possessive of Pronouns

In describing the bear, the author wrote:

"It snarled and whirled and gnashed its teeth . . ."

The word *its*, meaning "belonging to it," is the possessive form of the pronoun *it*.

Learn these possessive pronouns and their use:

POSSESSIVE PRONOUN	MEANING	USE
my and *mine*	(belonging to me)	It is *my* fault. The fault is *mine*.
your and *yours*	(belonging to you)	Is this *your* jacket? Is this jacket *yours*?
his	(belonging to him)	Johnny lost *his* key.
her and *hers*	(belonging to her)	This is *her* pen. This is *hers*.
its	(belonging to it)	A bird left *its* nest.
our and *ours*	(belonging to us)	Are these *our* tickets? Are these tickets *ours*?
their and *theirs*	(belonging to them)	Give them *their* share. Give them *theirs*.

You can see from the list above that NO APOSTROPHE is used with a *possessive pronoun*. Pay special attention to those ending in s. Like all other possessive pronouns, they are never written with an apostrophe.

RIGHT	*WRONG*
yours	your's
hers	her's
ours	our's
theirs	their's

On the other hand, a *possessive noun* DOES HAVE an apostrophe: the *boy's* ticket, the *girl's* share, etc.

Note again the use of the apostrophe in a possessive noun, but not in a possessive pronoun.

These notes are *Mary's*. (possessive *noun;* apostrophe)
These notes are *hers*. (possessive *pronoun;* no apostrophe)

Finally, do not confuse a possessive pronoun with a contraction. A contraction has an apostrophe, but a possessive pronoun—as stated before—does not.

CONTRACTIONS *(Apostrophe Required to Replace Omitted Letters)*	POSSESSIVE PRONOUNS *(No Apostrophe Required)*
It's (It is) late.	*Its* tail is short.
You're (You are) right.	*Your* brother came.
They're (They are) waiting.	*Their* work was done.

In the blank space, write the choice that makes the sentence correct.

1. The players took _____ places on the field. (*they're* or *their*?)

2. Let us know when _____ ready to leave. (*you're* or *your*?)

3. The owner of the jewel did not know _____ true value. (*its* or *it's*?)

4. Is the umbrella _____? (*her's* or *hers*?)

5. These are my keys. Where are _____? (*your's* or *yours*?)

6. Have you met my _____ husband? (*sisters* or *sister's*?)

7. _____ too bad you are ill. (*Its* or *It's*?)

8. Since our car is too small for all of us, let's ride in _____. (*yours* or *your's*?)

9. _____ is the second seat in the next row. (*Her's* or *Hers*?)

10. These sneakers must be _____. (*Tom's* or *Toms*?)

11. Do you know _____ parts? (*you're* or *your*?)

12. _____ a good chance of rain for tomorrow. (*Theirs* or *There's*?)

13. When the painter is done at your house, he will come to _____. (*ours* or *our's*?)

14. _____ was the better of the two talks. (*Your's* or *Yours*?)

15. Why won't you admit that _____ right? (*their* or *they're*?)

APOSTROPHE OR NO APOSTROPHE?

- **POSSESSIVE NOUN —** | APOSTROPHE REQUIRED |

  My *brother's* friend is a good tennis player.
  I saw your *neighbor's* lights were on.

- **CONTRACTION —** | APOSTROPHE REQUIRED |

  It's time for lunch!
  Do you know where *they're* going?

- **POSSESSIVE PRONOUN —** | NO APOSTROPHE |

  Ours is the stronger team.
  Theirs has been weakened by injuries.

READING SELECTION 4

When your parents have a quarrel, who usually wins, Mother or Father? Why?

from

Life With Father

by Clarence Day

One day while Father was in his office downtown, Auntie Gussie and Cousin Flossie arrived. Mother immediately began planning to take them to dine at the Waldorf, a much-talked-of new hotel at Fifth Avenue and Thirty-third Street, which she
5 very much wanted to see. She knew Father mightn't like the idea, but he would enjoy himself after he got there, and she thought she could manage him.

When he came in, she went to his bedroom to break the good news to him that instead of dining at home he was to go off on
10 a gay little party. She meant to do this diplomatically. But she wasn't an adept at coaxing or inveigling a man, and even if she had been, Father was not at all easy to coax. Whenever she was planning to manage him, the very tone of her voice put him on guard; it had an impatient note, as though really the only plan
15 she could think of was to wish he was manageable. So on this occasion, when she tried to get him in a good mood, he promptly got in a bad one. He looked suspiciously at Mother and said, "I don't feel well."

"You need a little change," Mother said. "That'll make you feel
20 better. Besides, Gussie's here and she wants to dine with us tonight at the Waldorf."

Father hated surprise attacks of this kind. No matter how placid he might be, he instantly got hot when one came. In less than a second he was rending the Waldorf asunder and saying what he thought of anybody who wanted to dine there. ₂₅

But Mother was fully prepared to see him take it hard at the start. She paid no attention to his vehement refusals. She said brightly that the Waldorf was lovely and that it would do him good to go out. There was no dinner at home for him anyway, so what else was there to do? ₃₀

When Father took in the situation, he undressed and put on his nightshirt. He shouted angrily at Mother that he had a sick headache. It made no difference to him whether there was any dinner or not. He couldn't touch a mouthful of food, he declared. Food be damned. What he needed was rest. After tottering around, ₃₅ putting his clothes away, he darkened his room. He climbed into bed. He pulled up the sheets, and he let out his breath in deep groans.

These startling blasts, which came at regular intervals, alarmed Auntie Gussie. But when she hurried down to help, ₄₀ Mother seemed annoyed and shooed her back up.

The next thing she knew, Mother impatiently called up to her that she was waiting. She had got tired of scolding Father and trying to make him get out of bed, and had made up her mind to dine at the Waldorf without him. She and Auntie Gussie and Flossie ₄₅ marched off by themselves. But they had to come back almost immediately because Mother didn't have enough money, and when she rushed into Father's sick-room and lit the gas again and made him get up and give her ten dollars, his roars of pain were terrific.

Line 11. *adept:* expert
Line 11. *inveigling:* leading on by trickery
Line 24. *asunder:* apart

Understanding What You Have Read

In the blank space, write the *letter* of the choice that best completes the statement.

1. Mother wants to dine at the Waldorf because _____.

   A. she is curious to see what the new hotel is like
   B. Aunt Gussie and Cousin Flossie have asked to be taken there
   C. she has not prepared dinner
   D. she feels that Father deserves a change

2. When Mother presents her idea to Father, she expects that he will _____.

   A. give in easily
   B. never accept it
   C. fight back hard at first
   D. suggest going to a different restaurant

3. Father's deep groans ___.

    A. have no effect on anyone
    B. frighten Mother
    C. show he needed rest very badly
    D. are part of an act

4. The passage suggests that Father ___.

    A. does not lose his temper easily
    B. is fond of Aunt Gussie
    C. considers dining at the Waldorf a waste of money
    D. has a poor appetite

5. The narrator appears to be ___.

    A. ashamed of his parents
    B. siding with Father
    C. taking Mother's side
    D. trying to report the incident without taking sides

Learning New Words

Line	Word	Meaning	Typical Use
12	**coax** *(v.)* 'kōks	influence by gentle urging or flattery; persuade by soothing words; wheedle	The mother tried to *coax* her child to come in from play, but he paid no attention to her gentle urging.
		(ant. **bully***)*	Use gentle words, not threats, as people do not like you to *bully* them.
10	**diplomatically** *(adv.)* ˌdip-lə-ˈmat-i-kə-lē	tactfully; without offending others	Some students hurt your feelings when they judge your work, as they do not know how to criticize *diplomatically*.
14	**impatient** *(adj.)* im-ˈpā-shənt	unwilling to bear delay or opposition; restless; short of temper	I asked them to wait a bit, but they were *impatient* and left quickly.
		(ant. **patient***)*	A young child cannot bear delay, but as he grows older he becomes more *patient*.
39	**interval** *(n.)* 'int-ər-vəl	space of time between two events; pause	There is an *interval* of four minutes between periods to permit students to go from one classroom to the next.

16	**mood** *(n.)* 'müd	state of mind; humor; disposition; temper	Dan said very little in class that day. He had just had a quarrel at home, and he was in a bad *mood*.
23	**placid** *(adj.)* 'plas-əd	calm; peaceful; free of disturbance	While Joe obviously was disturbed by the news, his brother seemed *placid*.
		(ant. **agitated**)	Something must have been disturbing Eileen; she looked *agitated*.
24	**rend** *(v.)* 'rend	pull apart violently; rip; tear	Pat is very displeased with the photograph. If she gets her hands on it, she will *rend* it to pieces.
41	**shoo** *(v.)* 'shü	cause to move away; scare away; drive away	She *shooed* the flies away with a sweep of her hand.
17	**suspiciously** *(adv.)* sə-'spish-əs-lē	in a *suspicious* (distrustful) manner; distrustfully; in a way that shows a lack of confidence	One shopper watched the salesclerk *suspiciously* as he was checking out her groceries; she was afraid he might overcharge her.
27	**vehement** *(adj.)* 'vē-ə-mənt	forceful; violent; showing strong feeling	The plan to do away with clubs and teams was dropped after *vehement* protests by students and parents.

Applying What You Have Learned

I. Which of the two choices makes the sentence correct? Write the *letter* of the correct answer in the space provided.

1. If you are impatient, you are unlikely to ____ your temper.

   A. lose   B. control

2. A ____ is a popular interval with employees.

   A. coffee break   B. retirement plan

3. He looked back suspiciously, as if he ____ us.

   A. had confidence in   B. didn't trust

4. The lake was so placid that _____.

    A. there was not a ripple on it   B. our boat was tossed about quite a bit

5. If you shoo away the pigeons, they will _____.

    A. eat out of your hand   B. only come back

6. When Derek returned the following fall, we noticed a change in his mood; he _____.

    A. had grown quite a bit   B. seemed much friendlier

7. You handled the matter diplomatically; no one was _____.

    A. offended   B. pleased

8. If coaxing fails, I may have to use _____.

    A. threats   B. flattery

9. This tale will rend _____.

    A. your heart   B. a great deal of interest

10. Her vehement reply _____.

    A. showed she was angry   B. could hardly be heard

II. The meaning of each expression below can be found in the vocabulary list on the next page. Find that meaning and write it in the space provided.

_____ 1. space of time between two events

_____ 2. showing strong feeling

_____ 3. without offending others

_____ 4. pull apart violently

_____ 5. scare away

_____ 6. influence by gentle urging

_____ 7. in a distrustful manner

_____ 8. free of disturbance

_____ 9. unwilling to bear delay

_____ 10. state of mind

impatient · placid
rend · coax
mood · interval
diplomatically · vehement
suspiciously · shoo

III. Synonyms and Antonyms

Fill the blanks in column A with the required synonyms or antonyms, selecting them from column B.

Column A   *Column B*

_____ 1. synonym for *disposition*   rend

_____ 2. antonym for *patient*   diplomatically

_____ 3. synonym for *rip*   vehement

_____ 4. synonym for *tactfully*   interval

_____ 5. synonym for *scare away*   placid

_____ 6. antonym for *bully*   shoo

_____ 7. synonym for *pause*   mood

_____ 8. synonym for *distrustfully*   coax

_____ 9. antonym for *agitated*   suspiciously

_____ 10. synonym for *forceful*   impatient

IV. Picture Quiz

In the blank space, write the *letter* of the picture that best fits the meaning of the sentence.

1. Of the three girls below, _____ seems the most vehement.

45

2. _____ is obviously impatient.

3. For an example of a placid water scene, look at _____.

Learning Some Derivatives

Each word in bold type below is a *root*. The words below it are its *derivatives*.

Note that *suspect,* when used as a *noun,* is pronounced 'səs-ˌpekt.

diplomat *(n.)*	You need the skill of a *diplomat* to keep opposing groups from fighting one another.
diplomatic *(adj.)*	You have to be *diplomatic* to maintain peace between opposing groups.
diplomatically *(adv.)*	You must be able to deal *diplomatically* with opposing groups.
diplomacy *(n.)*	It takes *diplomacy* to get opposing sides to work together.
impatient *(adj.)*	The audience was *impatient* for the film to begin.
impatiently *(adv.)*	The audience waited *impatiently* for the film to begin.
impatience *(n.)*	A few in the audience expressed their *impatience* by whistling.
mood *(n.)*	Why are you in a bad *mood*?
moody *(adj.)*	Why are you so *moody*?

46

placid *(adj.)*	She remained *placid* throughout the emergency.
placidly *(adv.)*	She continued to work *placidly* despite the trouble outside.
placidity *(n.)*	She was able to maintain her *placidity* all through the crisis.
rend *(v.)*	Baby's tears can *rend* Mother's heart.
rent *(n.)*	Baby's tearful plea can make a *rent* in Mother's heart.
suspect *(v.)*	Why do you *suspect* me?
suspicious *(adj.)*	Why are you *suspicious* of me?
suspiciously *(adv.)*	Why do you regard me *suspiciously*?
suspicion *(n.)*	Why do you look on me with *suspicion*?
suspect *(n.)*	Why do you consider me a *suspect*?
vehement *(adj.)*	I made a *vehement* denial of the charges against me.
vehemently *(adv.)*	I *vehemently* denied that I was in any way to blame.
vehemence *(n.)*	I asserted my innocence with *vehemence*.

I. Fill each blank with the word listed previously that best fits the meaning of the sentence.

1. Philip is entirely trustworthy. We have no reason to _____ him.

2. I could tell that Jane was in a hurry because she kept looking at her watch

   _____.

3. An ambassador is a(an) _____ of the highest rank.

4. Mother cannot understand how Dad can read his newspaper so _____

   while the children are fighting.

5. The _____ in the beach umbrella will get larger if it isn't patched soon.

6. When Mitchell's sister tried to switch the TV to another channel, he objected so

   _____ that she gave up the attempt.

7. In trying to settle a quarrel, you should not say anything that might offend either

   side. Be _____.

8. The captain was _____; he was subject to fits of temper.

9. War must be replaced by peace, _____ by trust, and hate by love.

10. My friend showed his _____ by shouting, "Hurry up! I can't wait

    for you all day!"

II. Synonyms

From the words listed previously, select the best *synonym* for each of the following:

1. forcefulness: _____

2. distrustful: _____

3. often in bad humor: _____

4. peaceful: _____

5. a lack of trust: _____

6. person imagined to be guilty: _____

7. tact: _____

8. opening resulting from tearing: _____

9. in a forceful manner: _____

10. tactful: _____

Improving Your Spelling: Suffixes After *-CE* and *-GE*

1. If a word ends in -CE or -GE, and the suffix added to it begins with A or O, do *not* drop the E.

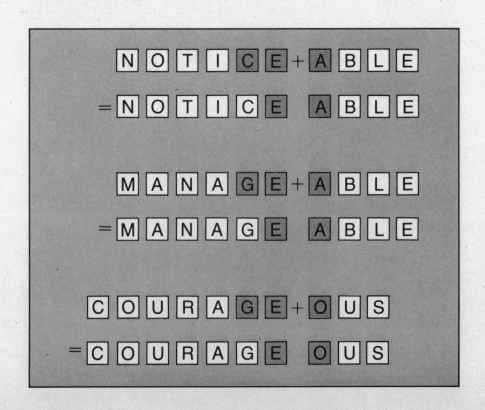

2. If the suffix begins with a vowel other than A or O, drop the E.

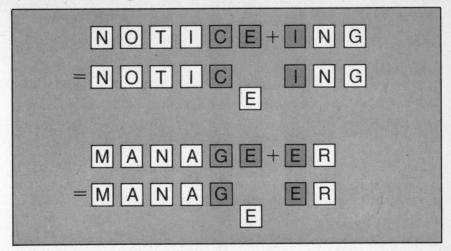

3. Of course, if the suffix begins with a consonant, do *not* drop the E.

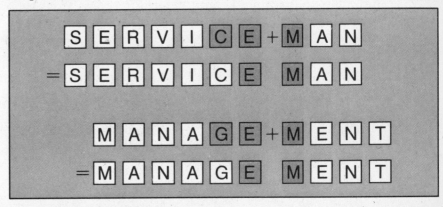

Fill in the blanks at the right:

1. change + able = _____

2. advantage + ous = _____

3. discharge + ing = _____

4. service + able = _____

5. manage + ing = _____

6. encourage + ment = _____

7. village + er = _____

8. replace + ing = _____

9. change + less = _____

10. replace + able = _____

11. outrage + ous = _____

12. peace + able = _____

13. enforce + ment = _____

14. change + ing = _____

15. exchange + able = _____

16. disadvantage + ous = _____

17. notice + ing = _____

18. recharge + able = _____

19. garage + man = _____

20. enforce + able = _____

Grammar: Pronouns After Prepositions

1. Many pronouns have more than one form, or *case*. The pronoun *I*, for example, also has the forms *me, my,* and *mine*.

    I is used as a subject.

I saw Brenda.	(*I* is subject of the verb *saw*.)
Joe and *I* saw Brenda.	(*I*, together with *Joe*, is subject of the verb *saw*.)
Brenda is shorter than *I*.	(*I* is subject of the understood verb *am:* Brenda is shorter than *I am*.)

    Me is used as an object.

Brenda saw *me*.	(*me* is object of the verb *saw*.)
Brenda saw Joe and *me*.	(*me*, together with *Joe*, is object of the verb *saw*.)

    My and *mine* are used to show possession.

      This is *my* glove.

      This glove is *mine*.

The following outline sums up the different forms, or *cases*, of the personal pronouns:

I *As a Subject* (known as NOMINATIVE CASE)	II *As an Object* (known as OBJECTIVE CASE)	III *As a Possessive* (known as POSSESSIVE CASE)
I	me	my, mine
you	you	your, yours
he	him	his
she	her	her, hers
it	it	its
we	us	our, ours
they	them	their, theirs

2. A *preposition* is a word that relates the noun or pronoun following it to some other word in the sentence:

He looked suspiciously *at* Mother.

The word *at,* above, is a *preposition.* It relates the noun *Mother* to the verb *looked.*

She wants to dine *with* us.

The word *with*, too, is a *preposition.* It relates the pronoun *us* to the verb *dine.*

The noun or pronoun after a preposition is called the *object of the preposition.* In the example above, the pronoun *us* is the object of the preposition *with.* In the previous example, the noun *Mother* is the object of the preposition *at.*

He looked suspiciously at Mother.
P.   O.P.

P. = preposition

O. P. = object of preposition

She wants to dine with us.
P.   O.P.

3. The following are some frequently used prepositions:

among	except	of
against	for	on
at	from	to
between	in	with
by	into	without

4. A pronoun after a preposition must be in the objective case (see column II on Page 50).

QUESTION: Everyone left except _____. (*I* or *me*?)

ANSWER: Everyone left except *me.*

EXPLANATION: The objective case *(me)* is required after the preposition *except.*
    Note that *except* is a preposition, just the same as *by* or *with.* A preposition requires the objective case after it. It would be just as wrong to say "except I" as to say "by I" or "with I."

Everyone left except me.
P.   O.P.

QUESTION: The class agreed with Mary and _____. (*he* or *him*?)

ANSWER: The class agreed with Mary and *him.*

EXPLANATION: The pronoun *him,* together with the noun *Mary,* is the object of the preposition *with; with* requires the objective case *him* (not *he*).

HINT: In a sentence like the previous one, construct two sentences. Then combine them for the correct answer.

SENTENCE 1: The class agreed with Mary.

SENTENCE 2: The class agreed with *him* (not *he*).

ANSWER: The class agreed with Mary and *him*.

The class agreed with Mary.
　　　　　　　　　 P.　 O.P.

The class agreed with him.
　　　　　　　　P.　 O.P.

The class agreed with Mary and him.
　　　　　　　　P.　　 ⌣compound⌣
　　　　　　　　　　　　 compound
　　　　　　　　　　　　 O.P.

REVIEW OF NOMINATIVE AND OBJECTIVE CASE OF PRONOUNS

NOMINATIVE

(1) **Subject of verb:**

　　S　　 V
　　We interviewed the Mayor.

(2) **Subject of understood verb:**

　　　　　　　　　　　　　　　　　 S
　　My sister earns as much money as *he*.
　　(The verb *does* or *earns* is understood.)

(3) **Compound subject:**

　　　　　　　　　 V
　　Mary and *I* painted the kitchen.
　　‿‿‿‿‿‿‿‿‿
　　　　S

OBJECTIVE

(4) **Direct object:**

　　S　　V　 D.O.
　　He called *me* last night.

(5) **Compound direct object:**

　　　　　　 S　　 V
　　The coach invited Tom and *us* to see the game.
　　　　　　　　　‿‿‿‿‿‿‿‿
　　　　　　　　　　 D.O.

52

I. Complete the sentence by inserting the correct nominative or objective form of the pronoun, as required.

1. Dad bought tickets for Miriam and _____. (*I* or *me*?)

2. Are you taller than _____? (*he* or *him*?)

3. Nobody complained except _____. (*he* or *him*?)

4. The committee consists of Kathy, Angela, and _____. (*I* or *me*?)

5. All expenses will be shared equally by you and _____. (*we* or *us*?)

6. Rhonda knows you can play the piano better than _____. (*she* or *her*?)

7. You and _____ have always gotten along well. (*they* or *them*?)

8. Wanda invited Terry and _____ to her party. (*I* or *me*?)

9. The Martins live on the same street as _____. (*we* or *us*?)

10. Has there been a quarrel between you and _____? (*they* or *them*?)

II. Fill in the missing forms of the italicized pronoun.

1. These are *my* notes. Give them to _____. They are _____, not yours.

2. This is *our* equipment. _____ own it. It belongs to _____. It is _____.

3. Let *them* sit in _____ own seats. These seats are ours, not _____.

4. *You* know what _____ share is. Marie and I have taken ours; the rest is _____.

5. *She* asked to use my typewriter because _____ is out of order, but I told _____ that I need it myself.

REVIEW OF GROUP I

I. Fill in the missing letters of the word at the right of the definition. Then write the complete word in the blank space.

DEFINITION	WORD	COMPLETE WORD
1. space of time	INTER ___ ___ ___	_____
2. person very greatly admired	___ D ___ L	_____
3. article of clothing	G ___ ___ MENT	_____
4. scare away	___ ___ OO	_____
5. in a misleading way	DE ___ ___ ___ TIVELY	_____
6. object thrown at a target	___ ___ SSILE	_____
7. sleep lightly	D ___ Z ___	_____
8. nervous laugh	T ___ TT ___ R	_____
9. covered with thick rough hair	SH ___ ___ GY	_____
10. fill with bewildered wonder	AST ___ ___ ND	_____
11. very nearly	PR ___ ___ TICALLY	_____
12. showing strong feeling	VEH ___ ___ ___ NT	_____
13. something required	___ ___ ___ ESSITY	_____
14. shelter from danger	___ ___ FUGE	_____
15. to a large extent	CONS ___ ___ ___ RABLY	_____
16. hang down	___ ___ OOP	_____
17. in a distrustful manner	___ ___ ___ PICIOUSLY	_____
18. unwilling to bear delay	IMP ___ ___ ___ ENT	_____
19. tactful person	___ ___ ___ LOMAT	_____
20. right or left side of a formation	FL ___ ___ K	_____

II. To each line below, add a word that has the *same meaning* as the first two words on the line. Choose your words from the vocabulary list on the next page.

1. calm, peaceful, _____

2. unoccupied, empty, _____

3. obstacle, hindrance, _____

4. face, oppose, _____

5. rip, tear, _____

6. sadden, discourage, _____

7. resentment, hostility, _____

8. expected, probable, _____

9. humor, disposition, _____

10. puzzle, perplex, _____

Vocabulary List

rend	baffle
animosity	depress
vacant	confront
placid	prospective
mood	obstruction

III. For each italicized word in column A, write the best *antonym* from column B.

	Column A	*Column B*
_____	1. feeling of *shame*	imaginative
_____	2. labored *effectively*	coax
_____	3. if costs *increase*	foolhardy
_____	4. entirely *believable*	indifferent
_____	5. moved *sluggishly*	futilely
_____	6. tried to *bully* us	diminish
_____	7. *matter-of-fact* account	pride
_____	8. a *wary* opponent	dense
_____	9. seemed *eager*	briskly
_____	10. *sparse* population	incredible

IV. Each line contains one misspelled word. Spell that word correctly in the space provided.

_____	1. aquainted, quantity, autumn
_____	2. everyone, encouragement, exausted
_____	3. surprise, bookeeper, noticing

_____ **4.** morgage, teammate, library

_____ **5.** probably, enforcable, nowhere

_____ **6.** roomate, fascinate, salmon

_____ **7.** nevertheless, playwright, reconize

_____ **8.** hereafter, symtom, doubtful

_____ **9.** receipt, goverment, someone

_____ **10.** candidate, serviceable, outragous

V. Complete each sentence below with the most appropriate word from the following vocabulary list.

Vocabulary List

diplomatically	placid	obstruction
missile	practically	futile
baffled	foolhardiness	prospective
incredible	dozed	drooped

1. Jeff told the _____ story of having seen a lion on Main Street.

2. There was no movement of air. Flags _____ . Not a leaf stirred.

3. Tickets for tonight's game are hard to get, as _____ all of them have been sold.

4. A double-parked delivery truck created a serious _____ to traffic.

5. From Dad's _____ expression I could tell that Mother had not yet told him of my breaking the window.

6. The movie must have bored you, since you _____ through half of it.

7. When the boys brought their dispute to Mr. Greenburg, he settled it so _____ that neither side was offended.

8. The _____ landed several yards beyond the target area.

9. To have driven across the tracks as the speeding train was approaching would have been the utmost of _____ .

10. The student's complaint was _____ , as his teacher refused to change his mark.

VI. On lines B and C, write the required forms of the italicized word on line A.

1. A. I am not a *deceiver*.

    B. I am not trying to _____ you.

    C. I am not trying to practice _____ on you.

2. A. Do not create an *obstruction* in our path.

    B. Don't be _____.

    C. Don't _____ our progress.

3. A. Belgium has a *dense* population.

    B. Belgium is _____ populated.

    C. Belgium has a high population _____.

4. A. Be *diplomatic*.

    B. Handle the matter _____.

    C. Use _____.

5. A. Wait. Don't be *impatient*.

    B. Don't be in a rush. Try to control your _____.

    C. There is no need to hurry. Stop behaving so _____.

6. A. Some people regard any change with *suspicion*.

    B. Some people are _____ of any change.

    C. Some people look _____ upon any change.

7. A. Is any tenant about to *vacate* an apartment?

    B. Will an apartment soon become _____?

    C. Will there be a _____ soon?

8. A. These problems are still *baffling*.

    B. These problems continue to _____ us.

    C. These are the same problems that have _____ us in the past.

9. A. Audrey is so *placid*. Nothing seems to disturb her.

    B. Audrey looked on _____ as my brother and I quarreled noisily.

    C. Nothing seems to disturb Audrey's _____.

10. A. Your Dad moved very *briskly*.

B. Your Dad surprised us by his _____ of motion.

C. Your Dad took very _____ strides.

11. A. He did not realize the *futility* of trying to put out the fire by himself.

B. He did not realize that it was _____ to try to put out the fire by himself.

C. He _____ attempted to put out the fire by himself.

12. A. The news may *depress* them.

B. They may find the news _____ .

C. The news may give them a feeling of _____ .

13. A. Higher costs will make a tax increase *necessary*.

B. Higher costs will _____ a tax increase.

C. Increased taxes will become a _____ if costs continue to rise.

14. A. His *vehement* "no" showed that he was angry.

B. His anger showed itself by the _____ with which he turned down our request.

C. He _____ refused our request.

15. A. Light travels at the *incredible* speed of 186,000 miles per second.

B. Light is _____ swift.

C. Have you ever wondered at the _____ of the speed of light?

16. A. How can anyone remain *indifferent* to the sufferings of others?

B. How can anyone regard the sufferings of others with _____ ?

C. How can anyone look _____ on the sufferings of others?

17. A. The weatherman now considers tomorrow as a *prospectively* rainy day.

B. The _____ of rain makes our plans for tomorrow uncertain.

C. The _____ rain may force us to change our plans.

18. A. So far, the detectives have found no one whom they regard *suspiciously*.

B. So far, the detectives do not _____ anyone.

C. So far, the detectives have no _____ .

19. A. The facts were in front of me all the time, but I didn't see them. I must have been *dense*.

B. I remained _____ ignorant of the facts, though they were right before my eyes.

C. I am ashamed of my _____ in failing to perceive the obvious facts.

20. A. It takes tact and *diplomacy* to bring opposing sides together.

B. You must be tactful and _____, if you are to bring the opposing sides together.

C. If you are to get the opposing sides to agree, you must be a tactful person, as well as a _____.

GROUP II / Reading Selections 5–8

READING SELECTION 5

Have you ever known anyone who unfortunately could communicate only in sign language? Here are two such people.

from

The Heart Is a Lonely Hunter

by Carson McCullers

IN THE TOWN there were two mutes, and they were always together. Early every morning they would come out from the house where they lived and walk arm in arm down the street to work. The two friends were very different. The one who always steered
5 the way was an obese and dreamy Greek. In the summer he would come out wearing a yellow or green polo shirt stuffed sloppily into his trousers in front and hanging loose behind. When it was colder he wore over this a shapeless gray sweater. His face was round and oily, with half-closed eyelids and lips that curved in
10 a gentle, stupid smile. The other mute was tall. His eyes had a quick, intelligent expression. He was always immaculate and very soberly dressed.

Every morning the two friends walked silently together until they reached the main street of the town. Then when they came to
15 a certain fruit and candy store they paused for a moment on the sidewalk outside. The Greek, Spiros Antonapoulos, worked for his cousin, who owned this fruit store. His job was to make candies and sweets, uncrate the fruits, and keep the place clean. The thin mute, John Singer, nearly always put his hand on his friend's
20 arm and looked for a second into his face before leaving him. Then after this good-bye Singer crossed the street and walked on alone to the jewelry store where he worked as a silverware engraver.

In the late afternoon the friends would meet again. Singer came back to the fruit store and waited until Antonapoulos was ready to go home. The Greek would be lazily unpacking a case of peaches or melons, or perhaps looking at the funny paper in the kitchen behind the store where he cooked. Before their departure Antonapoulos always opened a paper sack he kept hidden during the day on one of the kitchen shelves. Inside were stored various bits of food he had collected—a piece of fruit, samples of candy, or the butt-end of a liverwurst. Usually before leaving Antonapoulos waddled gently to the glassed case in the front of the store where some meats and cheeses were kept. He glided open the back of the case and his fat hand groped lovingly for some particular dainty inside which he had wanted. Sometimes his cousin who owned the place did not see him. But if he noticed he stared at his cousin with a warning in his tight, pale face. Sadly Antonapoulos would shuffle the morsel from one corner of the case to the other. During these times Singer stood very straight with his hands in his pockets and looked in another direction. He did not like to watch this little scene between the two Greeks. For, excepting drinking and a certain solitary secret pleasure, Antonapoulos loved to eat more than anything else in the world.

In the dusk the two mutes walked slowly home together. At home Singer was always talking to Antonapoulos. His hands shaped the words in a swift series of designs. His face was eager and his gray-green eyes sparkled brightly. With his thin, strong hands he told Antonapoulos all that had happened during the day.

Antonapoulos sat back lazily and looked at Singer. It was seldom that he ever moved his hands to speak at all—and then it was to say that he wanted to eat or to sleep or to drink. These three things he always said with the same vague, fumbling signs.

Line 35. *dainty:* something delicious

Understanding What You Have Read

In the blank space, write the *letter* of the choice that best completes the statement according to the selection.

1. Antonapoulos _____.

A. has a weak character
B. is neat
C. pays no attention to his cousin's warnings
D. has many subjects to talk about

2. Singer ＿＿.

    A. is fond of drinking
    B. has very little to say
    C. is always in a hurry
    D. seems intelligent

3. The two friends not only leave for work together but also ＿＿.

    A. work for the same employer
    B. have lunch together
    C. come home together
    D. tell each other all that happened during the day

4. The owner of the fruit store ＿＿.

    A. watches Antonapoulos to prevent him from stealing
    B. is very unfair to Antonapoulos
    C. knows that Antonapoulos is stealing, but does not try to stop him
    D. does not know that Antonapoulos is stealing

5. Antonapoulos ＿＿.

    A. is a hard worker
    B. shows laziness both at home and at work
    C. is lazy at home but not at work
    D. is lazy at work but not at home

Learning New Words

Line	Word	Meaning	Typical Use
27	**departure** (*n.*) di-ˈpär-chər	act of going away; leaving; setting out	Our *departure* from the airport was delayed for two hours because of fog.
		(*ant.* **arrival**)	My aunt and uncle greeted me warmly on my *arrival* at their home.
34	**grope** (*v.*) ˈgrōp	search blindly or uncertainly; feel one's way	We *groped* our way slowly down the darkened stairs.
11	**immaculate** (*adj.*) im-ˈak-yə-lət	spotless; absolutely clean	There was not a speck of dirt or dust in the room; it was *immaculate*.
38	**morsel** (*n.*) ˈmȯr-səl	small piece of food; bit; fragment	All that was left of the two-pound salami was a *morsel* of three or four ounces.

1	**mute** *(n.)* 'myüt	person who is *mute* (unable to speak); one who cannot or does not speak	*Mutes* are able to speak to one another through hand signs.
5	**obese** *(adj.)* ō-'bēs	extremely fat; stout; corpulent	One member of the comedy team was very slim, and the other was just the opposite—*obese*.
		(ant. **skinny***)*	
46	**series** *(n.)* 'sir-ēz	group of similar things or events coming one after the other; sequence; succession	Each side has won three games. Today's contest will be the final and deciding game in the *series* of seven.
38	**shuffle** *(v.)* 'shəf-əl	1. move about from one place to another; shift	We stood on a long line, and as we moved up, we *shuffled* our baggage along with us.
		2. walk without lifting the feet	Near the end of the hike we were so weary that we *shuffled* rather than walked.
12	**soberly** *(adv.)* 'sō-bər-lē	in a *sober* (plain) manner; not flashily	The son wore a flashy sports jacket and slacks of the latest cut, but the father was *soberly* dressed in a gray business suit.
		(ant. **gaily***)*	Store windows are *gaily* decorated for the Christmas shopping season.
42	**solitary** *(adj.)* 'säl-ə-,ter-ē	without companions; away from people; lonely	One of the most awful punishments a prisoner can suffer is to be placed in *solitary* confinement.

Applying What You Have Learned

I. Which of the two choices makes the sentence correct? Write the *letter* of the correct answer in the space provided.

1. The new shirt was as immaculate as ＿＿.

    A. freshly fallen snow   B. a glove

2. The obese patient was advised by her physician to ＿＿.

    A. eat between meals   B. lose weight

3. You would not expect to find ＿＿ in a soberly furnished room.

    A. plain furniture   B. bright colors

4. He needs a ____, not a morsel.

A. pair of sneakers   B. loaf of bread

5. My aunt lived a solitary life; she ____ had visitors.

A. often   B. seldom

6. When we grope, we ____.

A. cannot see our way clearly B. cannot go astray

7. The following is a good example of a series: ____.

A. spring, summer, autumn, winter   B. Better late than never

8. ____; don't be vague.

A. Wait till we get there   B. Give us clear instructions

9. Don't shuffle; ____.

A. lift your feet   B. take your time

10. A mute is unlikely to ____.

A. read a newspaper   B. need a telephone

II. The meaning of each expression below can be found in the vocabulary list on the next page. Find that meaning and write it in the space provided.

_____ **1.** a person who cannot speak

_____ **2.** a small piece of food

_____ **3.** in a plain manner

_____ **4.** extremely fat

_____ **5.** away from people

_____ **6.** search blindly

_____ **7.** move about from one place to another

_____ **8.** absolutely clean

_____ **9.** act of going away

_____ **10.** group of similar things coming one after the other

morsel	series
solitary	grope
immaculate	obese
shuffle	mute
departure	soberly

III. Synonyms and Antonyms

Fill the blanks in column A with the required synonyms or antonyms, selecting them from column B.

Column A   *Column B*

_____ **1.** synonym for *fragment*   grope

_____ **2.** antonym for *skinny*   departure

_____ **3.** synonym for *lonely*   mute

_____ **4.** antonym for *arrival*   shuffle

_____ **5.** synonym for *succession*   obese

_____ **6.** antonym for *gaily*   immaculate

_____ **7.** synonym for *shift*   soberly

_____ **8.** synonym for *feel one's way*   morsel

_____ **9.** synonym for *absolutely clean*   series

_____ **10.** synonym for *one unable to speak*   solitary

IV. Picture Quiz

In the blank space, write the *letter* of the picture that best fits the meaning of the sentence.

1. ____ can be considered obese.

2. With _____, a wall can be made immaculate.

D

E

F

3. _____ is groping his way.

G

H

I

Learning Some Derivatives

Each word in bold type below is a *root*. The words below it are its *derivatives*.

depart *(v.)*	Your bus *departs* for Boston at 9:10 tomorrow morning.
departure *(n.)*	I will be at the terminal to see you before your *departure*.
immaculate *(adj.)*	Mrs. Kelly is an *immaculate* housekeeper.
immaculately *(adv.)*	Her home is *immaculately* maintained.
immaculateness *(n.)*	She prides herself on her *immaculateness*.
mute *(adj.)*	Ann made no reply; she was *mute* to all my inquiries.
mutely *(adv.)*	When I questioned her, she stared *mutely* at the ceiling.
mute *(n.)*	"Surely," I said, "you have the power of speech. You are not a *mute*."
muteness *(n.)*	At last she broke her *muteness* and said: "Go away."

obese *(adj.)*	If you overeat, you may become *obese*.
obesity *(n.)*	Overeating may cause *obesity*.
series *(n.)*	What is the next number in the *series* 2 . . . 4 . . . 6 . . . ?
serial *(adj.)*	In your report, page 5 comes before page 4, and page 12 is before page 11. Please put your pages in *serial* order.
serial *(n.)*	Channel 3 will do a *serial* on the adventures of Sherlock Holmes on Fridays at 8:30 P.M.
serialize *(v.)*	Channel 3 will *serialize* the adventures of Sherlock Holmes on Fridays at 8:30 P.M.
sober *(adj.)*	A Caribbean cruise on a luxury liner would not appeal to my uncle; he is a person of *sober* tastes.
soberly *(adv.)*	He prefers to live *soberly*.
soberness *(n.)*	A visit to a night club or a gambling casino would be out of keeping with the *soberness* of his way of life.
solitary *(adj.)*	At night, the building will be deserted, save for a *solitary* caretaker.
solitude *(n.)*	He expects to have a dog with him to reduce his *solitude*.

Fill each blank below with the word listed previously that best fits the meaning of the sentence.

1. When you feel that you have been unfairly treated, speak up. Don't remain _____ .

2. Most people do not enjoy _____; they prefer to be with others.

3. Mother thought the tie I wanted to get Dad was too loud. She urged me to select a more _____ pattern.

4. The curtains were returned by the cleaner _____ laundered.

5. Before you _____, we will call to say good-bye.

6. Helen Keller was stricken with blindness, deafness, and _____ when she was less than two years old.

7. At the factory, each new appliance receives a(an) _____ number in the order of its manufacture.

8. Overeating may lead to _____.

9. The magazine will _____ the new novel by printing successive installments in the next six issues.

10. "If you visit our kitchens," said the restaurant owner, "you will be impressed with their _____."

Improving Your Spelling:
Forming Plurals of Nouns Ending in *-F* or *-Fe*

1. Some nouns ending in F or FE form the plural in the regular way by adding S.

SINGULAR	PLURAL
belief	belief*s*
safe	safe*s*

Here are some more nouns that form the plural regularly. Write the plural in the space at the right.

brief   _____

chief   _____

giraffe   _____

grief   _____

handkerchief   _____

proof   _____

roof   _____

sheriff   _____

staff   _____

2. Some nouns ending in F or FE change the F or FE to V and add ES.

SINGULAR	PLURAL
lea*f*	lea*ves*
kni*fe*	kni*ves*

Here are some more nouns that form the plural in the same way as *leaf* and *knife*. Write the plural in the space at the right.

calf   _____

half   _____

life   _____

loaf   _____

self   _____

shelf   _____

thief   _____

wife   _____

wolf   _____

Complete each sentence by writing the plural of the most appropriate noun selected from the lists in this lesson.

1. How many _____ of bread can you buy for a dollar?

2. In the early autumn the _____ begin to fall.

3. Our library now has more than 8,000 books on its _____.

4. Surely you don't believe that a cat has nine _____.

5. Banks store cash in their vaults and _____.

6. Some watched the parade from the _____ of their homes.

7. Do you know how to arrange spoons, forks, and _____ when setting a table?

8. Considerate people use their _____ to cover their coughs and sneezes.

9. Before coming to America, the Puritans suffered because of their religious _____.

10. The _____ of the police and fire departments were called to a meeting at City Hall.

Correct Usage: Distinguishing Between *Loose* and *Lose*

Learn the difference between *loose* and *lose*.

Loose means "free," or "not fastened."

"In the summer he would come out wearing a yellow or green polo shirt stuffed sloppily into his trousers in front and hanging *loose* behind."

To *lose* means "to mislay," "be deprived of," "fail to get" or "fail to win."

How did you *lose* your wallet?

Complete each of the following sentences by adding *loose* or *lose*.

1. Tighten the handle; it's _____.

2. Stand in line, or you may _____ your turn.

3. Win or _____, we shall still be friends.

4. Junior made us look at his _____ tooth.

5. Plant in the spring, when the soil is _____.

6. The Greens are moving. We are sorry to _____ them.

7. Was the dog _____, or on a leash?

8. With these directions, you cannot _____ your way.

9. Did you _____ your homework again?

10. What would happen if the lion were to break _____?

What would your parents say if they learned you were planning to leave home to see the world? In the following passage, Robinson Crusoe tells how his father reacted in a similar situation.

from

Robinson Crusoe

by Daniel Defoe

After this, he pressed me earnestly, and in the most affectionate manner, not to play the young man, not to precipitate myself into miseries which Nature and the station of life I was born in seemed to have provided against; that I was under no necessity of seeking my bread; that he would do well for me, and endeavor to enter me 5
fairly into the station of life which he had been just recommending to me; and that if I was not very easy and happy in the world, it must be my mere fate or fault that must hinder it, and that he should have nothing to answer for, having thus discharged his duty in warning me against measures which he knew would be to 10
my hurt. In a word, that as he would do very kind things for me if I would stay and settle at home as he directed, so he would not have so much hand in my misfortunes as to give me any encouragement to go away. And to close all, he told me I had my elder brother for an example, to whom he had used the same earnest 15
persuasions to keep him from going into the Low Country wars, but could not prevail, his young desires prompting him to run into the army where he was killed; and though he said he would not cease to pray for me, yet he would venture to say to me that if I did take this foolish step, God would not bless me, and I 20
would have leisure hereafter to reflect upon having neglected his counsel when there might be none to assist in my recovery.

I observed in this last part of his discourse, which was truly

prophetic, though I suppose my father did not know it to be so
25 himself; I say, I observed the tears run down his face very plenti-
fully, and especially when he spoke of my brother who was killed;
and that when he spoke of my having leisure to repent, and none
to assist me, he was so moved that he broke off the discourse and
told me his heart was so full he could say no more to me.

Line 2. *precipitate:* hurl

Understanding What You Have Read

In the blank space write the *letter* of the choice that best completes the statement or answers the question according to the
selection.

1. The father ____.

   A. does not try to influence Robinson's thinking
   B. has stopped mourning for Robinson's elder brother
   C. is not able to hide his feelings
   D. makes no predictions about Robinson's future

2. The passage suggests that the Crusoe family is ____.

   A. not poor
   B. unable to pay its debts
   C. not highly respected
   D. large

3. The elder brother of Robinson Crusoe ____.

   A. followed his father's advice
   B. went to sea
   C. was forced to earn his own bread
   D. became a soldier

4. As used in the first sentence, the phrase "to play the young man" most probably
   means to act ____.

   A. after careful consideration
   B. recklessly
   C. like a coward
   D. selfishly

5. According to the passage, which of the following is most likely to happen later? ____

   A. The elder brother will return home.
   B. The father will encourage Robinson Crusoe to leave home.
   C. The father will stop praying for Robinson Crusoe.
   D. Robinson Crusoe will suffer a great deal.

Learning New Words

Line	Word	Meaning	Typical Use
1	**affectionate** (adj.) ə-'fek-shə-nət	feeling or showing a great liking for a person or persons; loving; devoted; tender	At the airport, the soldier received an *affectionate* welcome by relatives who hugged and kissed him.
		(*ant.* **cold, undemonstrative**)	Mr. Farrel is proud of his children, though he doesn't show it openly. He is an *undemonstrative* person.
22	**counsel** (n.) 'kaun-səl	1. advice	You would not have made this error if you had followed my *counsel*.
		2. lawyer engaged in the trial of a case; attorney	Before answering the question, the witness conferred with his *counsel*.
9	**discharge** (v.) dis-'chärj	perform; fulfill; carry out	If elected, I will *discharge* my responsibilities to the best of my ability.
23	**discourse** (n.) 'dis-ˌkōrs	talk; conversation; communication of ideas by talking	It is usually better to have a face-to-face *discourse* than to write or telephone.
1	**earnestly** (adv.) 'ər-nəst-lē	in an *earnest* (serious; not playful) manner; seriously; zealously	Ever since he failed the test, Jeff has been doing his assignments *earnestly*.
		(*ant.* **frivolously**)	Before selecting a career, give it serious consideration. Do not choose *frivolously*.
5	**endeavor** (v.) in-'dev-ər	try; make an effort; strive	The defeated candidate is not discouraged; he will *endeavor* to win the next election.
17	**prevail** (v.) pri-'vāl	1. urge successfully (usually with *on* or *upon*); persuade	I finally *prevailed* upon John to lend me his science notes.
		2. gain the advantage; win; triumph	Before the fight, I thought the stronger of the two boys would *prevail*.
17	**prompt** (v.) 'prämpt	cause (someone to do something); move to action; provoke	My high fever and loss of appetite *prompted* Mother to call our physician.

24	**prophetic**	having the characteristics of	Jules Verne's novel TWENTY

24   **prophetic**   having the characteristics of   Jules Verne's novel TWENTY
     (adj.)   a *prophecy* (prediction of the   THOUSAND LEAGUES UN-
     prə-'fet-ik   future); foretelling future   DER THE SEA was *prophetic;*
          events; predictive   it foreshadowed the invention
             of the submarine.

27   **repent** *(v.)*   feel sorry for an error or sin;   Many a dropout has later *re-*
     ri-'pent   regret   *pented* his decision to quit school.

Applying What You Have Learned

I.   Which of the two choices makes the sentence correct? Write the *letter* of the correct answer in the space provided.

1. That was a long discourse. I did not know you could ____ so much.

   A. run   B. talk

2. The affectionate parent greeted her child with ____.

   A. an embrace   B. silence

3. Something prompted Carl to leave the examination suddenly, but I do not know the ____.

   A. cause   B. penalty

4. Paul repented his harsh remarks to his sister. He ____.

   A. would not take back one word of it   B. wanted to apologize

5. When you needed counsel, there was no one to ____ you.

   A. advise   B. recommend

6. The ____ is the one who prevails.

   A. loser   B. winner

7. In the past I ____, but now I am working earnestly.

   A. was very serious   B. joked most of the time

8. You said you would endeavor to do your best, but you haven't shown even the slightest ____.

   A. effort   B. appreciation

9. Our Mayor deserves to be _____ for discharging his duties.

    A. criticized   B. praised

10. What the coach said last year was prophetic. We have just won the championship, _____.

    A. as he had predicted   B. in spite of his doubts

II. The meaning of each expression below can be found in the vocabulary list at the bottom of the exercise. Find that meaning and write it in the space provided.

_____   **1.** in a serious manner

_____   **2.** carry out

_____   **3.** feel sorry for an error or sin

_____   **4.** urge successfully

_____   **5.** move to action

_____   **6.** communication of ideas by talking

_____   **7.** showing a great liking for a person

_____   **8.** make an effort

_____   **9.** lawyer engaged in the trial of a case

_____   **10.** foretelling future events

Vocabulary List

counsel	repent
endeavor	prevail
prompt	earnestly
affectionate	prophetic
discharge	discourse

III. Synonyms and Antonyms

Fill the blanks in column A with the required synonyms or antonyms, selecting them from column B.

	Column A	Column B
_____	1. synonym for *regret*	prevail
_____	2. synonym for *conversation*	discharge
_____	3. antonym for *cold*	prophetic
_____	4. synonym for *triumph*	affectionate
_____	5. synonym for *advice*	earnestly
_____	6. synonym for *predictive*	repent
_____	7. antonym for *frivolously*	prompt
_____	8. synonym for *try*	counsel
_____	9. synonym for *perform*	endeavor
_____	10. synonym for *cause*	discourse

IV. Picture Quiz

In the blank space, write the *letter* of the picture that best fits the meaning of the sentence.

1. ____ prevailed.

A

HIS BOUT WITH THE CHAMPION ENDED IN A DRAW.

B

CAME OUT FIRST IN THE SCHOOL POETRY CONTEST.

C

HAD TO DROP OUT OF THE RACE BECAUSE OF ENGINE TROUBLE.

2. ____ is having a discourse.

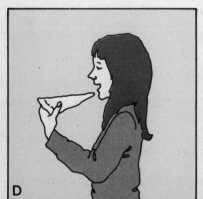

D

E

F

3. ____ is an affectionate scene.

  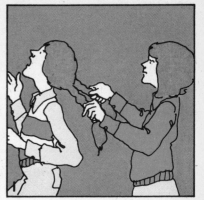

Learning Some Derivatives

Each word in bold type below is a *root*. The words below it are its *derivatives*. Note the difference in pronunciation and spelling between the verb *prophesy,* pronounced ˈpräf-ə-ˌsī, and the noun *prophecy,* pronounced ˈpräf-ə-sē.

affection *(n.)*	If you show Fido that you like him, he will give you a great deal of *affection.*
affectionate *(adj.)*	Fido is an *affectionate* dog.
affectionately *(adv.)*	Fido licks my hand *affectionately.*
counsel *(n.)*	When I needed advice, you kindly offered me good *counsel.*
counsel *(v.)*	It was thoughtful of you to *counsel* me when I needed advice.
counselor *(n.)*	I was glad to have you as my *counselor.*
discharge *(v.)*	On Inauguration Day, the President must take an oath that he will *discharge* his duties faithfully.
discharge *(n.)*	The President must swear that he will be faithful in the *discharge* of his duties.
earnest *(adj.)*	Bob was *earnest* when he said he would lend you the money; he wasn't joking.
earnestly *(adv.)*	Bob *earnestly* wanted to lend you the money.
earnestness *(n.)*	The proof of Bob's *earnestness* is that he brought the money the next day.
endeavor *(v.)*	This fall I will *endeavor* to get on the track team.
endeavor *(n.)*	If my *endeavor* fails, I will make a second attempt when tryouts are held again.

prophet *(n.)*	I cannot foretell the future, since I am not a *prophet*.
prophetic *(adj.)*	Some people, however, can predict what will happen; they have *prophetic* vision.
prophetically *(adv.)*	Washington *prophetically* warned us to stay out of entangling foreign alliances. For a young nation, it proved to be good advice.
prophesy *(v.)*	The "experts" *prophesy* we will lose the championship.
prophecy *(n.)*	We hope their *prophecy* does not come true.
repent *(v.)*	How can we forgive him if he does not *repent* his attempts to hurt us?
repentant *(adj.)*	If he were really *repentant,* he would have said that he is sorry for the way he acted.
repentantly *(adv.)*	He would have come to us *repentantly* and asked us to forgive him.
repentance *(n.)*	But he has not taken back one word of what he said against us; he has shown no *repentance*.

Fill each blank below with the word listed previously that best fits the meaning of the sentence.

1. I will not venture to foretell the future, since I am no _____.

2. We thought Valerie would be sorry for the trouble she had caused, but she was not the least bit _____.

3. Harvey came to me for advice, but I felt I was not the right person to _____ him.

4. The umpires showed good judgment in the _____ of their duties.

5. Her first _____ ended in failure, but she will make another attempt.

6. The sisters are cold to each other. There seems to be no _____ at all between them.

7. After his mother became ill, the son felt a deep _____ for the suffering he had needlessly caused her.

8. My _____ advised me to take Spanish as my first foreign language.

9. I didn't vote for Steve because he is too frivolous. In my opinion he lacks the _____ necessary to be a good leader.

10. The weatherman's _____ of heavy showers proved accurate.

Improving Your Spelling: More About the Suffix -LY

Robinson Crusoe relates that what his father had told him proved to be "*truly* prophetic."

1. Note that the adjective *true,* contrary to what we might expect, drops its silent E before the suffix -LY:

true + ly = truly

Two more adjectives that behave the same way are *due* and *whole.*

due + ly = duly

whole + ly = wholly

2. Other adjectives ending in silent E do *not* drop that letter before -LY.

vague + ly = vague*l*y

affectionate + ly = affectionat*e*ly

3. But adjectives ending in a *consonant plus* -LE (*able, ample, gentle,* etc.) drop the final E and add only a Y.

probable − *e* + *y* = probably

4. Adjectives ending in Y change the Y to I before -LY:

happy + ly = happ*i*ly

Exceptions: slyly, shyly, dryly

5. Adjectives ending in -IC add AL plus LY:

prophetic + al + ly = prophetic*ally*

I. Change the following adjectives to adverbs:

ADJECTIVE	ADVERB
1. immaculate	_____
2. whole	_____
3. necessary	_____
4. incredible	_____
5. specific	_____
6. earnest	_____
7. true	_____
8. fatal	_____
9. uneasy	_____

ADDING -LY TO ADJECTIVES

Review these ways of forming an adverb by adding -LY to an adjective.
(Numbers at the left refer to the rules explained in this lesson.)

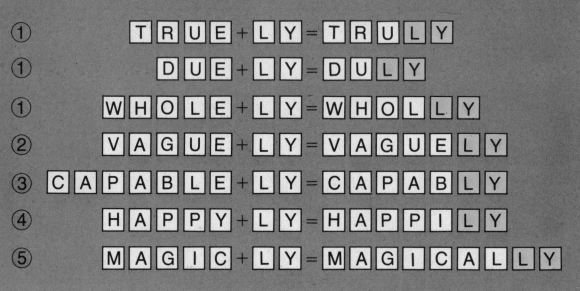

① TRUE + LY = TRULY

① DUE + LY = DULY

① WHOLE + LY = WHOLLY

② VAGUE + LY = VAGUELY

③ CAPABLE + LY = CAPABLY

④ HAPPY + LY = HAPPILY

⑤ MAGIC + LY = MAGICALLY

10. democratic   _____

11. respectful   _____

12. diplomatic   _____

13. abrupt   _____

14. humble   _____

15. due   _____

16. regretful   _____

17. considerable   _____

18. shy   _____

19. exceptional   _____

20. magic   _____

II. Change the following adverbs to adjectives:

ADVERB   ADJECTIVE

1. unhappily   _____

2. gratefully   _____

3. tragically   _____

4. soberly   _____

5. prophetically   _____

6. wholly   _____

7. easily   _____

8. agreeably   _____

9. truly   _____

10. usually   _____

11. brutally   _____

12. duly   _____

13. ably   _____

14. futilely   _____

15. gradually   _____

16. terrifically   _____

17. sensibly   _____

18. outrageously   _____

19. slyly   _____

20. gently   _____

Correct Usage: *Good* and *Well*

Robinson Crusoe's father promised to "do *well*" for his son.

1. Note that *well,* above, is an adverb. It modifies the verb *do.* Here are some more examples of the use of *well* as an adverb.

> Sam throws *well.* (adverb—modifies verb *throws*)
> I know him *well.* (adverb—modifies verb *know*)

2. But *well* can be an adjective, too, meaning "healthy," or "not ill."

> We are glad you are *well.*   (adjective—modifies pronoun *you*)
> My aunt is not a *well* person. (adjective—modifies noun *person*)

3. *Good,* on the other hand, is an adjective.

> This is a *good* dinner. (adjective — modifies noun *dinner*)
> The food tastes *good.* (adjective — modifies noun *food*)

4. Note that both of the following are correct:

> I feel *good.*
> I feel *well.*

However, the two expressions do not have the same meaning.

> *I feel good* means "I feel happy" or "in high spirits."
> *I feel well* means "I feel healthy" or "in good health."

| WELL | may be used as both an adjective and an adverb. |

> He is now a *well* man. (modifies noun *man*)
> ADJ.

> She played her part *well.* (modifies verb *played*)
> ADV.

| GOOD | can be used only as an adjective. |

> Father made a *good* deal. (modifies noun *deal*)
> ADJ.

Complete each sentence by inserting *well* or *good* in the blank space.

1. I didn't do too _____ in the tryouts for the baseball team.

2. Pam has a fever; she is not _____.

3. The old car still runs _____.

4. I felt _____ when I learned that I had passed all my subjects.

5. The food looks very _____ to me.

6. Do your younger brothers behave _____ when you have visitors?

7. The news sounds _____.

8. He's just an acquaintance; I do not know him _____.

9. The milk may have turned sour; it doesn't smell _____.

10. Ever since her hip injury, Grandma has not been able to walk too _____.

The boy telling the story has been instructed by the captain to watch for "a seafaring man with one leg." Therefore, when a blind stranger appears one day, the boy at first suspects nothing.

from

Treasure Island

by Robert Louis Stevenson

So things passed until, the day after the funeral, and about three o'clock of a bitter, foggy, frosty afternoon, I was standing at the door for a moment, full of sad thoughts about my father, when I saw someone drawing slowly near along the road. He was plainly blind, for he tapped before him with a stick and wore a 5 great green shade over his eyes and nose; and he was hunched, as if with age or weakness, and wore a huge old tattered sea-cloak with a hood that made him appear positively deformed. I never saw in my life a more dreadful-looking figure. He stopped a little from the inn, and raising his voice in an odd sing-song, 10 addressed the air in front of him, "Will any kind friend inform a poor blind man, who has lost the precious sight of his eyes in the gracious defence of his native country, England—and God bless King George!—where or in what part of this country he may now be?" 15

"You are at the Admiral Benbow, Black Hill Cove, my good man," said I.

"I hear a voice," said he, "a young voice. Will you give me your hand, my kind young friend, and lead me in?"

I held out my hand, and the horrible, soft-spoken, eyeless 20 creature gripped it in a moment like a vise. I was so much startled that I struggled to withdraw, but the blind man pulled me close up to him with a single action of his arm.

"Now, boy," he said, "take me in to the captain."

25 "Sir," said I, "upon my word I dare not."

"Oh," he sneered, "that's it! Take me in straight or I'll break your arm."

And he gave it, as he spoke, a wrench that made me cry out.

"Sir," said I, "it is for yourself I mean. The captain is not
30 what he used to be. He sits with a drawn cutlass. Another gentleman——"

"Come, now, march," interrupted he; and I never heard a voice so cruel, and cold, and ugly as that blind man's. It cowed me more than the pain, and I began to obey him at once, walking
35 straight in at the door and towards the parlour, where our sick old buccaneer was sitting, dazed with rum. The blind man clung close to me, holding me in one iron fist and leaning almost more of his weight on me than I could carry. "Lead me straight up to him, and when I'm in view, cry out, 'Here's a friend for you, Bill.'
40 If you don't, I'll do this," and with that he gave me a twitch that I thought would have made me faint. Between this and that, I was so utterly terrified of the blind beggar that I forgot my terror of the captain, and as I opened the parlour door, cried out the words he had ordered in a trembling voice.

45 The poor captain raised his eyes, and at one look the rum went out of him and left him staring sober. The expression of his face was not so much of terror as of mortal sickness. He made a movement to rise, but I do not believe he had enough force left in his body.

Line 36. *buccaneer:* pirate

Understanding What You Have Read

In the blank space, write the *letter* of the choice that best completes the statement.

1. The boy who tells the story ____ .

   A. makes no effort to get away from the blind man
   B. has never had any fear of the captain
   C. has just lost his father
   D. does as he is told, without protest

2. The blind man ____ .

   A. knows where the captain is staying
   B. is a friend of the captain
   C. frightens the boy, but does not hurt him
   D. does not know the way to the "Admiral Benbow"

3. When the blind man appears before him, the captain _____.

    A. is too drunk to recognize him
    B. doesn't even look up
    C. makes no attempt to move
    D. suffers a severe shock

4. What frightens the boy most of all is the blind man's _____.

    A. threat to break his arm
    B. voice
    C. demand to see the captain
    D. appearance

5. The boy may best be described as _____.

    A. selfish and cunning
    B. untrustworthy and cowardly
    C. fearless and reckless
    D. trusting and polite

Learning New Words

Line	Word	Meaning	Typical Use
11	**address** (v.) ə-'dres	direct one's words to; deliver a speech to; speak to	The President usually *addresses* the nation on radio and television when he is about to make an important announcement.
36	**cling** (v.) 'kliŋ	hold on tightly; hold fast; adhere; stick	Johnny couldn't swim, but he managed to keep afloat by *clinging* to the overturned boat.
36	**daze** (v.) 'dāz	stun; confuse and bewilder; stupefy	When one of Lou's punches landed squarely on my nose, I fell back, *dazed* by the blow.
8	**deform** (v.) di-'fòrm	spoil the shape or appearance of; disfigure	It is a pity when a pretty face is *deformed* by thoughts of envy, hatred, or bitterness.
13	**native** (adj.) 'nāt-iv	1. belonging to a person because of his birth	Since Grandfather was born in Rome, his *native* land is Italy.
		2. inborn; natural	Robert Burns had very little schooling, but a high *native* intelligence.
		3. grown or having its origin in a particular region.	The potato is *native* to American soil.

		(*ant.* **alien, foreign**)	The newcomer spoke only Spanish. English to him was an *alien* tongue.
8	**positively** *(adv.)* 'päz-ət-iv-lē	extremely; absolutely; in a *positive* (definite) way	We were very tired when we set out, and by the time we got to our destination we were *positively* exhausted.
7	**tattered** *(adj.)* 'tat-ərd	1. torn to shreds; ragged	Rod returned from playing football, his face bruised and his clothes *tattered*.
		2. wearing torn and ragged clothes	Refugees streamed into the emergency relief center, many of them barefoot and *tattered*.
42	**terrified** *(adj.)* 'ter-ə-ˌfīd	filled with *terror* (intense fear); frightened very much; alarmed	When a snake glided across Sandy's path, she became *terrified* and screamed.
42	**terror** *(n.)* 'ter-ər	intense fear; dread	Before I learned to swim, I had a *terror* of the water because I had once nearly drowned.
22	**withdraw** *(v.)* wi<u>th</u>-'drȯ	1. draw back; go away; leave	If you want to *withdraw* from our committee, we will gladly permit you to leave.
		2. take back; remove	Please *withdraw* my name. I do not wish to be a candidate.
		(*ant.* **introduce**)	At the last session, our Congressman *introduced* four bills to control pollution.

Applying What You Have Learned

I. Which answer makes the sentence correct? Write the *letter* of the correct answer in the space provided.

1. The fans were dazed by the _____ .

   A. fairness of the decision   B. stunning upset

2. We tried to withdraw but there was no way to get _____ .

   A. in   B. out

3. He looked as terrified as if he had just seen a _____ .

   A. ghost   B. rainbow

4. Isn't it about time that you got rid of your tattered ___?

A. sweatshirt B. pen

5. Your native language is the language of the country where ___.

A. you live B. you were born

6. There is ___ chance she may change her mind, as long as she is not positively opposed to joining us.

A. little B. some

7. Jack wanted to ___, but he had nothing to cling to.

A. hold on B. let go

8. I would have addressed the man if I had not ___.

A. forgotten my pen B. been too nervous to speak

9. Most people wake up in terror when ___.

A. they have a nightmare B. the alarm clock rings

10. Will the injured leg remain deformed or will it regain its ___?

A. shape B. strength

II. The meaning of each expression below can be found in the vocabulary list on the next page. Find that meaning and write it in the space provided.

_____ **1.** spoil the shape of

_____ **2.** take back

_____ **3.** hold on tightly

_____ **4.** torn to shreds

_____ **5.** direct one's words to

_____ **6.** in a definite way

_____ **7.** belonging to a person because of his birth

_____ **8.** frightened very much

_____ **9.** confuse and bewilder

_____ **10.** intense fear

Vocabulary List

terrified	tattered
positively	withdraw
cling	native
daze	deform
address	terror

III. Synonyms and Antonyms

Fill the blanks in column A with the required synonyms and antonyms, selecting them from column B.

Column A   *Column B*

_____ 1. synonym for *tattered*   daze

_____ 2. synonym for *stupefy*   native

_____ 3. synonym for *dread*   positively

_____ 4. antonym for *alien*   terror

_____ 5. synonym for *disfigure*   address

_____ 6. synonym for *frightened*   withdraw

_____ 7. synonym for *speak to*   ragged

_____ 8. antonym for *introduce*   cling

_____ 9. synonym for *absolutely*   terrified

_____ 10. synonym for *stick*   deform

IV. Picture Quiz

In the blank space, write the letter of the picture that best fits the meaning of the sentence.

1. _____ may become tattered.

88

2. ____ is a clinging plant.

3. ____ may be used in addressing a group.

Learning Some Derivatives

Each word in bold type below is a *root*. The words below it are its *derivatives*.

address *(v.)*   Mr. Baker will *address* the Astronomy Club.

address *(n.)*   The topic of his *address* will be "The Hidden Side of the Moon."

daze *(v.)*   I was *dazed* when I heard that Berlinger's is going out of business.

daze *(n.)*   The news of Berlinger's closing left me in a *daze*.

deform *(v.)*   Infantile paralysis used to cripple and *deform* thousands of people every year.

deformed *(adj.)*   This disease struck Franklin D. Roosevelt and left him *deformed*.

deformity *(n.)*   The discovery of a vaccine against infantile paralysis has freed millions of people from fear of suffering and *deformity*.

positive *(adj.)*   Yesterday, I said that I "might" come. I was sorry I could not be more *positive*.

positively (adv.)	Now, I know that I *positively* cannot attend.
positiveness (n.)	Now, I can say with *positiveness* that I shall be unable to attend the meeting.
tatter (n.)	When Eric returned from his football game, his face was muddy and his clothes were in *tatters*.
tattered (adj.)	Mother will probably use his *tattered* clothes for rags.
terrify (v.)	Horror films may *terrify* a young child.
terrifying (adj.)	Ghosts, witches, and monsters like Dracula and Frankenstein are *terrifying* to many children.
terrified (adj.)	*Terrified* youngsters sometimes scream while watching a horror film.
terror (n.)	For centuries, the Barbary pirates spread *terror* in the Mediterranean Sea.
terrorize (v.)	They *terrorized* the merchant vessels of those nations that did not pay them tribute.
terrorism (n.)	In 1815, an American fleet defeated the Barbary pirates, ending their *terrorism* against American shipping.
terrorist (n.)	The airplane hijacker is a twentieth-century pirate. Since he uses the passengers and crew as hostages, he must be considered a *terrorist*.
withdraw (v.)	Instead of joining in the conversation, Joe *withdrew* into a corner.
withdrawn (adj.)	I was surprised, because he is not usually shy or *withdrawn*.
withdrawal (n.)	Noticing his *withdrawal,* I went over to talk with him.

Fill each blank with the word listed previously that best fits the meaning of the sentence.

1. You did not realize what you were doing; you must have been in a(an) _____.

2. A beggar in _____s appeared at the king's court.

3. A child, _____ by the smoke, was hiding under a bed, where fortunately a fireman found him.

4. At first the new student was shy and _____, but he soon began to make friends.

5. The President's _____ will be on radio and television tonight.

6. When the _____ was arrested, a store of explosives was found in his basement.

90

7. You have not given us a very _____ statement of what you saw. Can you please be more definite?

8. Most banks will permit you to make a deposit or _____ by mail.

9. One of our teammates has a limp, but he plays well in spite of his _____ .

10. My first ride on a Ferris Wheel was a(an) _____ experience. I was frightened to death.

Improving Your Spelling:

Distinguishing Between Homonyms

Homonyms are words that are alike in pronunciation but different in spelling and meaning.

Review these sets of homonyms:

brake (stopping device): Step on the *brake*.
break (fracture): How did you *break* your arm?

its (belonging to it): The dog licked *its* paw.
it's (it is): Can't you see *it's* raining?

pain (suffering): John complained about the *pain* in his arm.
pane (sheet of glass): Who broke the *pane* in the storm window?

passed (went by): She *passed* me in the corridor a moment ago.
past (beyond): Go *past* the next corner.
past (time gone by): Can you remember the *past*?

sight (vision): The old man has lost the precious *sight* of his eyes.
site (space of ground): Has a *site* been chosen for the new building?

straight (free from curves): A ruler has a *straight* edge.
strait (narrow waterway): Where is the *Strait* of Gibraltar?

there (in that place): When will you be *there*?
their (belonging to them): They ate *their* lunch.
they're (they are): They said that *they're* coming.

to (in the direction of and reaching): Jerry walks *to* school.
too (also): Gail wants to stop. Do you want to stop, *too*?
too (excessively): Open a window. It's *too* hot in here.
two (one plus one): The price is *two* dollars.

wait (delay): We can *wait* no longer.
weight (heaviness): Labels on packaged foods state the *weight* of the contents.

your (belonging to you): "Will you give me *your* hand?"
you're (you are): Tell us what *you're* planning.

Complete each sentence below by inserting the correct homonym:

1. I went _____ home. (straight, strait)

2. Have you gained any _____? (wait, weight)

3. Miss Stark liked my composition, except for _____ ending. (it's, its)

4. Months have _____ since I last saw him. (passed, past)

5. How much will it cost to replace the broken _____? (pain, pane)

6. Money has been voted to purchase an athletic field _____. (sight, site)

7. Are they bringing _____ gloves? (there, their, they're)

8. Do you realize what _____ saying? (your, you're)

9. Be careful not to _____ the point. (brake, break)

10. I'd like something to eat. Are you hungry _____? (too, two)

Grammar: More About Adverbs

"He was *plainly* blind . . ."

1. Most adverbs, like *plainly* above, are formed by adding *-ly* to the adjective.

ADJECTIVE   ADVERB

plain + ly = plain*ly*
real + ly = real*ly*

2. Some adverbs do not add *-ly*. They are spelled the same as adjectives.

Lead me *straight* up to him. (modifies verb *lead*)
ADV.

This is a *straight* line. (modifies noun *line*)
ADJ.

Here are some additional words like *straight* that have the same spelling as adjective and adverb. Fill in the blank spaces in the adverb column.

	ADJECTIVE	ADVERB
SAMPLE:	straight	**straight**
	better	_____
	early	_____
	fast	_____
	hard	_____
	late	_____
	low	_____
	near	_____

3. Some adverbs have two spellings: (1) the same as the adjective, and (2) the adjective plus *-ly:*

    (1) The blind man clung *close* to me.
    (2) The blind man clung *closely* to me.

Below are several words like *close* that have two spellings as adverbs. Fill in the blank spaces in the adverb column.

	ADJECTIVE		ADVERB
SAMPLE:	close	**close** or	**closely**
	bright	_____ or	_____
	cheap	_____ or	_____
	deep	_____ or	_____
	fair	_____ or	_____
	high	_____ or	_____
	loose	_____ or	_____
	loud	_____ or	_____
	right	_____ or	_____
	rough	_____ or	_____
	slow	_____ or	_____
	smooth	_____ or	_____
	tight	_____ or	_____
	wrong	_____ or	_____

SPELLINGS OF ADVERBS

(1) Most adverbs are formed by adding -LY to the adjective.

       Our team is a *sure* winner.
          ADJ.

       She *surely* was happy to see you.
       ADV.

(2) Some adverbs are spelled the same as the adjective.

       The *early* bird catches the worm.
       ADJ.

       Several parents arrived *early*.
                ADV.

(3) Some adverbs may be spelled the same as the adjective *or* with -LY added.

       Talk *loud* (or *loudly*) so that all of us can hear you.
       ADV.   ADV.

Each first sentence below has a word in italics used as an adjective. If the *same* word—with *no change* in spelling—can be used as an adverb, write it in the blank space in the second sentence. If not, write the form ending in *-ly*.

SAMPLE: It was a *close* race.
Stay **close** to me.

SAMPLE: Don is a *careful* worker.
Don does his work **carefully.**

1. It was a *bright* day.

   The sun shone _____.

2. This is the *right* way to do it.

   Do it _____.

3. Bea is a *skillful* speaker.

   Bea speaks _____.

4. We took a *straight* route.

   We went _____ home.

5. Write a *better* composition.

   Can't you write _____?

6. The play was a *terrific* success.

   The play was _____ successful.

7. It was a *slow* train.

   The train went _____.

8. The nurses were *immaculate*.

   The nurses were _____

   dressed.

9. The plane was at a *low* altitude.

   The plane was flying _____.

10. The cover should be *tight*.

    The cover should fit _____.

11. The *whole* building was destroyed.

    The building was _____ destroyed.

12. She spoke in a *loud* voice.

    She spoke too _____.

13. Milk is *cheap*.

    Milk can be bought _____.

14. You pronounced my name the *wrong* way.

    You pronounced my name _____.

15. Joel has made *considerable* improvement.

    Joel is _____ improved.

16. The strap was *loose*.

    The strap hung _____.

17. This is a *true* pleasure.

    We are _____ pleased.

18. We went to the *early* show.

    We went _____.

Kino has a precious pearl to sell, but he cannot get a fair price for it in his own village. Therefore, with his wife Juana and their infant Coyotito, he has begun the long and difficult journey to Mexico City. Suddenly he discovers that he is being followed.

from

The Pearl

by John Steinbeck

And then he saw them moving along. His body stiffened and he drew down his head and peeked out from under a fallen branch. In the distance he could see three figures, two on foot and one on horseback. But he knew what they were, and a chill of fear went
5 through him. Even in the distance he could see the two on foot moving slowly along, bent low to the ground. Here, one would pause and look at the earth, while the other joined him. They were the trackers, they could follow the trail of a bighorn sheep in the stone mountains. They were as sensitive as hounds. Here, he and
10 Juana might have stepped out of the wheel rut, and these people from the inland, these hunters, could follow, could read a broken straw or a little tumbled pile of dust. Behind them, on a horse, was a dark man, his nose covered with a blanket, and across his saddle a rifle gleamed in the sun.
15 Kino lay as rigid as the tree limb. He barely breathed, and his eyes went to the place where he had swept out the track. Even the sweeping might be a message to the trackers. He knew these inland hunters. In a country where there was little game they managed to live because of their ability to hunt, and they were
20 hunting him. They scuttled over the ground like animals and found a sign and crouched over it while the horseman waited.

The trackers whined a little, like excited dogs on a warming trail. Kino slowly drew his big knife to his hand and made it ready.

He knew what he must do. If the trackers found the swept place, he must leap for the horseman, kill him quickly and take the rifle. That was his only chance in the world. And as the three drew nearer on the road, Kino dug little pits with his sandaled toes so that he could leap without warning, so that his feet would not slip. He had only a little vision under the fallen limb. 25

Now Juana, back in her hidden place, heard the pad of the horse's hoofs, and Coyotito gurgled. She took him up quickly and put him under her shawl. 30

When the trackers came near, Kino could see only their legs and only the legs of the horse from under the fallen branch. He saw the dark horny feet of the men and their ragged white clothes, and he heard the creak of leather of the saddle and the clink of spurs. The trackers stopped at the swept place and studied it, and the horseman stopped. The horse flung his head up against the bit and the bit-roller clicked under his tongue and the horse snorted. Then the dark trackers turned and studied the horse and watched his ears. 35 40

Kino was not breathing, but his back arched a little and the muscles of his arms and legs stood out with tension and a line of sweat formed on his upper lip.

Understanding What You Have Read

In the blank space, write the *letter* of the choice that best completes the statement.

1. When Kino sees the men in the distance, he realizes that ____.

    A. they will not be able to find him
    B. he has no chance to escape
    C. they have been sent to find him and kill him
    D. they know exactly where he is hiding

2. The author does NOT compare the trackers to ____.

    A. sheep
    B. hounds
    C. animals
    D. dogs

3. The trackers ____.

    A. do not worry Kino
    B. show signs of becoming discouraged
    C. follow behind the horseman
    D. look to the horse for a clue

4. The passage suggests that ____.

    A. Juana is worried that Coyotito may betray their hiding place
    B. the trackers have rifles

C. Kino is barefoot

D. there are many wild animals in the area

5. The expression "a warming trail," as used in the first sentence of the third paragraph, means a trail that ____.

A. is losing its freshness

B. leads into the sun

C. seems increasingly likely to be the right trail

D. becomes increasingly harder to follow

Learning New Words

Line	Word	Meaning	Typical Use
15	**barely** *(adv.)* 'be(ə)r-lē	hardly; by the narrowest margin; scarcely	You turned the TV down so low that I could *barely* hear it.
21	**crouch** *(v.)* 'kraủch	stoop low with legs bent; bend low	Everyone stood straight except Roscoe, who was *crouching,* apparently to tie a shoe lace.
18	**game** *(n.)* 'gām	animals hunted for sport or food; quarry	The hunters crouched in the tall grass, waiting for their *game* to appear.
15	**limb** *(n.)* 'lim	1. large branch of a tree	During the storm, a heavy elm *limb* fell on two parked cars, wrecking them.
		2. arm, leg, or wing	You say you fractured a *limb* last year? Was it an arm or a leg?
7	**pause** *(v.)* 'póz	stop temporarily; hesitate; wait	The pupil who read too quickly was advised to *pause* briefly at the end of each sentence.
15	**rigid** *(adj.)* 'rij-əd	stiff; not bending; inflexible; hard	Foam-cushioned seats are much more comfortable than *rigid* wooden benches.
		(ant. **flexible***)*	Plastic toys are not so *flexible* as toys made of rubber.
9	**sensitive** *(adj.)* 'sen-sə-tiv	1. receiving impressions readily	Our watchdog barks at the approach of strangers while they are still a good way off; she is a *sensitive* animal.

		2. easily affected or moved (usually followed by *to*)	Dad always stops to help when he sees someone in trouble. He is *sensitive* to the plight of others.
		3. easily hurt	Pam is a very *sensitive* child; if you scold her ever so slightly, she will begin to cry.
		(*ant.* **insensitive, callous**)	How can you be so *insensitive* as to quarrel with Paul when he is ill? Have you no feelings?
			I thought Tom might be hurt by my criticism, but I was wrong; he is quite *callous*.
43	**tension** *(n.)* 'ten-shən	1. stretched condition; degree of stiffness; tautness	Guitar strings break when tightened to an abnormal *tension*.
		2. state of mental unrest; nervous strain; stress	With the score tied and less than a minute to play, the *tension* on both sides was almost unbearable.
29	**vision** *(n.)* 'vizh-ən	power of seeing; sight	Since she began using her new glasses, Susan's *vision* has improved greatly.
		(*ant.* **blindness**)	
22	**whine** *(v.)* 'hwīn	utter a high-pitched complaining cry or sound; complain in an irritable, childish way	My little nephew used to *whine* when he talked, so that he always sounded as if he were complaining.

Applying What You Have Learned

I. Which of the two choices makes the sentence correct? Write the *letter* of the correct answer in the space provided.

1. I was under such tension that I ____ .

A. bit my fingernails   B. fell asleep

2. When game is plentiful, there is no shortage of ____ .

A. sports   B. meat

3. ____ may reduce a driver's vision.

A. A dirty windshield   B. Worn tires

4. I crouched to ____.

   A. read the notice posted above the chalkboard

   B. look at the titles on the bottom shelf

5. When a dog whines, it is a sign that ____.

   A. something is bothering him

   B. he is happy and content

6. With an income of $61.25 and expenses of ____, our club last year barely managed to make ends meet.

   A. $87.50

   B. $59.75

7. I did not injure a limb; I bruised my ____.

   A. leg

   B. chin

8. If we pause, we shall ____.

   A. overtake the leader

   B. fall behind

9. A ____ is not rigid.

   A. rubber band

   B. brick chimney

10. Lou ____; he is very sensitive.

   A. does not care what others may say

   B. is easily offended

II. The meaning of each expression below can be found in the vocabulary list on the next page. Find that meaning and write it in the space provided.

_____ **1.** stop temporarily

_____ **2.** state of mental unrest

_____ **3.** not bending

_____ **4.** receiving impressions readily

_____ **5.** by the narrowest margin

_____ **6.** animals hunted for sport or food

_____ **7.** utter a high-pitched complaining cry

_____ **8.** arm, leg, or wing

_____ **9.** stoop low with legs bent

_____ **10.** power of seeing

Vocabulary List

sensitive	rigid
crouch	vision
tension	barely
pause	limb
whine	game

III. Synonyms and Antonyms

Fill the blanks in column A with the required synonyms or antonyms, selecting them from column B.

Column A   *Column B*

_____ 1. synonym for *hesitate*   tension

_____ 2. antonym for *blindness*   limb

_____ 3. synonym for *stress*   rigid

_____ 4. synonym for *quarry*   whine

_____ 5. antonym for *flexible*   barely

_____ 6. synonym for *branch*   crouch

_____ 7. synonym for *hardly*   vision

_____ 8. antonym for *callous*   pause

_____ 9. synonym for *complain*   sensitive

_____ 10. synonym for *bend low*   game

IV. Picture Quiz

In the blank space, write the *letter* of the picture that best fits the meaning of the sentence.

1. There is no limb in scene _____.

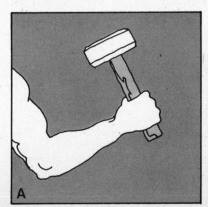
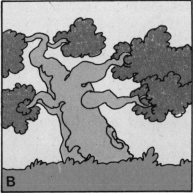

101

2. ____ is crouching.

3. ____ is flexible.

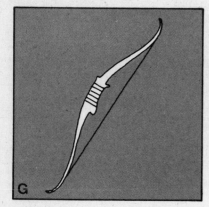

Learning Some Derivatives

Each word in bold type below is a *root*. The words below it are its *derivatives*.

bare *(adj.)*	I made the deadline by *bare* seconds.
barely *(adv.)*	I *barely* managed to get my application in on time.
crouch *(v.)*	If I *crouch,* my back doesn't ache when I get up.
crouch *(n.)*	However, Dad's back sometimes hurts him when he gets up from a *crouch.*
pause *(v.)*	Since we have been driving for nearly two hours, let us *pause* for some refreshment.
pause *(n.)*	After a brief *pause* for lunch, we will continue with our trip.
rigid *(adj.)*	Nancy is going to be *rigid* in sticking to her diet.
rigidly *(adv.)*	She has told me that she will *rigidly* avoid all fattening foods.
rigidity *(n.)*	She should certainly lose weight if she follows her diet with *rigidity.*

sensitive *(adj.)*	One of my teeth is painfully *sensitive*.
sensitively *(adv.)*	It reacts more *sensitively* to cold than to heat.
sensitivity *(n.)*	The dentist says that, after the tooth is treated, the *sensitivity* should disappear.
tense *(adj.)*	Some of the passengers became *tense* when their plane continued to circle over the airport, awaiting permission to land.
tensely *(adv.)*	The pilot, too, waited *tensely* for instructions from the control tower.
tension *(n.)*	If not for the fog, there would have been no delays and, therefore, no *tension*.
vision *(n.)*	People of *vision* try to make an educated guess of what conditions will be like in the future.
envision *(v.)*	They try to *envision* tomorrow's needs today.
revision *(n.)*	Their guess may need *revision* — it may be too high or too low — but it is better to plan ahead than to live blindly.
whine *(v.)*	Did you hear the wind *whine* through the trees?
whine *(n.)*	Listen to the *whine* of the wind.

Fill each blank below with the word on the list above that best fits the meaning of the sentence.

1. I was very _____ when I began my speech; the nervous strain was almost too much for me.

2. In a race it is much better to start from a(an) _____ than from a standing position.

3. My teacher said that, looking ahead, he could _____ a bright future for me.

4. The batting championship was decided by the _____ margin of one thousandth of a percentage point.

5. Knowing your sister's _____, I was extremely careful not to say anything that might hurt her feelings.

6. Anyone could have seen that I was nervous as I paced _____ up and down the hospital corridor.

7. Your composition needs _____; you should look it over again to make corrections and improvements.

8. When troops are reviewed, they are supposed to stand _____ at attention.

9. The _____ of sirens was a sign that the fire engines were approaching.

10. After a brief _____ for a commercial, the program will continue.

Improving Your Spelling:
Words Ending in -LE, -EL, -AL, and -FUL

1. Words usually end in -LE, rather than -EL.

rifle	tumble	simple	ample
saddle	tickle	pickle	angle
muscle	bottle	candle	article
gurgle	sample	nozzle	particle
giggle	ankle	handle	wrangle
baffle	dwindle	shuffle	principle (rule)

2. A few end in -EL.

label	panel	bushel
model	parcel	morsel
nickel	cancel	travel
level	gravel	colonel
barrel	quarrel	counsel (advice)

3. Review these words ending in -AL.

sandal	final	brutal	gradual
metal	special	material	usual
fatal	original	general	mortal
approval	natural	actual	official
renewal	additional	arrival	principal (chief)

4. Adjectives end in -FUL, rather than -FULL.

awful	grateful
beautiful	useful, etc.

Exception: the adjective *full* itself.

One word on each line is misspelled. Spell it correctly in the space at the right.

1. wonderful, special, nickle, bushel _____

2. gradual, quarrle, additional, full _____

3. barrel, angle, level, peacefull   _____

4. dwindel, sample, useful, little   _____

5. aweful, saddle, final, panel   _____

6. brutal, tearful, sandle, model   _____

7. usual, painfull, simple, muscle   _____

8. careful, counsel, morsel, baffel   _____

9. lable, hopeful, natural, handle   _____

10. pickle, ankel, joyful, fatal   _____

Grammar: Agreement of Subject and Verb

1. A singular subject requires a singular verb. A plural subject requires a plural verb.

    A. The *horseman was* not in a hurry.
    B. The *trackers were* not in a hurry.

The singular subject *horseman* requires the singular verb *was*. The plural subject *trackers* requires the plural verb *were*.

    C. *Kino knows* his business.
    D. The *trackers know* their business.

The singular subject *Kino* requires the singular verb *knows*. The plural subject *trackers* requires the plural verb *know*.

2. Note that verbs ending in *s* are usually singular: *is, was, knows, has, does, eats, sleeps,* etc.

3. Normally the subject comes before the verb. In the following cases, however, you will find the **subject after the verb:**

    A. In a question:

        Are the *boys* home yet?
         V   S

        (The subject is *boys.*)

    B. In a sentence beginning with *There is, There are, Here is, Here are,* etc.

        There *is food* on the table.
           V   S

        (The subject is *food,* not *there.*)

Here *are* your *friends*.

    V   S

(The subject is *friends*, not *here*.)

4. An *of*-phrase between a subject and its verb has no effect on agreement.

A box of cookies is on the shelf.

Reading the above sentence without the phrase *of cookies*, we have:

A *box is* on the shelf.

   S V

The singular subject *box* requires the singular verb *is*.

However, note the following:

The *cookies are* on the shelf.

     S   V

Here, the plural subject *cookies* requires the plural verb *are*.

AGREEMENT OF SUBJECT AND VERB

The diagrams below illustrate agreement between subject and verb. Numbers at the left refer to the model sentences in this lesson. In each diagram, the subject is to the left of the vertical line, and the verb to the right.

The horseman was not in a hurry.

1A

horseman	was
(singular subject)	(singular verb)

Are the boys home yet?

3A

boys	are
(plural subject)	(plural verb)

The trackers were not in a hurry.

1B

trackers	were
(plural subject)	(plural verb)

There is food on the table.

3B

food	is
(singular subject)	(singular verb)

Kino knows his business.

1C

Kino	knows
(singular subject)	(singular verb)

Here are your friends.

3B

friends	are
(plural subject)	(plural verb)

The trackers know their business.

1D

trackers	know
(plural subject)	(plural verb)

A box of cookies is on the shelf.

4

box	is
(singular subject)	(singular verb)

In each sentence below there is a subject without a verb. If that subject is singular, select a singular verb for it. If it is plural, choose a plural verb. Write the correct verb in the space provided.

1. Here (is, are) _____ a pint of blueberries.

2. There (was, were) _____ three persons in Kino's family.

3. (Where's, Where are) _____ your gloves?

4. The supermarket (doesn't, don't) _____ open until 8 A.M.

5. A bunch of carrots (sells, sell) _____ for twenty-five cents.

6. (There's, There are) _____ several reasons for starting early.

7. How much (has, have) _____ prices gone up?

8. A flock of birds (was, were) _____ feeding in the meadow.

9. (Doesn't, Don't) _____ she know the correct answer?

10. One of our players (seems, seem) _____ to be hurt.

REVIEW OF GROUP II

I. Fill in the missing letters of the word at the right of the definition. Then write the complete word in the blank space.

DEFINITION	WORD	COMPLETE WORD
1. spoil the shape of	DEF _ _ _	_____
2. feel sorry for an error or sin	_ _ PENT	_____
3. make an effort	END _ _ VOR	_____
4. animals hunted	_ _ ME	_____
5. torn to shreds	TAT _ _ _ ED	_____
6. absolutely clean	_ _ _ ACULATE	_____
7. move to action	PR _ _ PT	_____
8. frighten very much	_ _ _ RIFY	_____
9. state of mental unrest	TENS _ _ _	_____
10. urge successfully	_ _ EVAIL	_____
11. feel one's way	GR _ _ _	_____
12. power of seeing	_ _ SION	_____
13. intense fear	TER _ _ _	_____
14. large branch of a tree	_ _ MB	_____
15. complain in an irritable way	WHI _ _	_____
16. person who cannot speak	MU _ _	_____
17. foretelling future events	_ _ _ PHETIC	_____
18. stoop low with legs bent	_ _ OUCH	_____
19. direct one's words to	ADDR _ _ _	_____
20. walk without lifting the feet	_ _ UFFLE	_____

II. To each line below, add a word that has the *same meaning* as the first two words on the line. Choose your words from the vocabulary list below.

1. perform, fulfill, _____

2. scarcely, hardly, _____

3. sequence, succession, _____

4. stun, stupefy, _____

5. hesitate, wait, _____

6. bit, fragment, _____

7. stick, adhere, _____

8. talk, conversation, _____

9. extremely, absolutely, _____

10. lawyer, attorney, _____

Vocabulary List

series	barely
positively	discourse
discharge	morsel
cling	daze
counsel	pause

III. For each italicized word in column A, write the best *antonym* from column B.

Column A		*Column B*
_____	1. *cold* greeting	sensitive
_____	2. at our *arrival*	soberly
_____	3. *callous* person	withdraw
_____	4. often *accompanied*	departure
_____	5. *alien* custom	rigid
_____	6. *introduce* a motion	affectionate
_____	7. becoming *skinny*	obese
_____	8. acted *frivolously*	native
_____	9. *flexible* plan	earnestly
_____	10. *gaily* decorated	solitary

IV. A. Fill in the missing letters of the incomplete word in column A. Then write the complete word in column B.

Column A   *Column B*

1. Ask them for th __ __ __ names and addresses.   _____

2. Mother has a pa __ __ ful headache.   _____

3. Please take some. I have t __ o much.   _____

4. Never ride in a car with faulty br __ __ __ s.   _____

5. I know Chicago. I used to live th __ __ __.   _____

6. Read the directions printed on the lab __ __.   _____

7. Poison! Fat __ __ if swallowed!   _____

8. Who is the princip __ __ of your school?   _____

9. Does the first question baff __ __ you?   _____

10. Who has two nick __ __ s for a dime?   _____

B. Write the plural in the space provided.

SINGULAR   PLURAL

11. leaf   _____

12. knife   _____

13. belief   _____

14. handkerchief   _____

15. thief   _____

C. Change each of the following adjectives to an adverb ending in *-ly:*

ADJECTIVE   ADVERB

16. easy   _____

17. true   _____

18. terrific   _____

19. brutal   _____

20. whole   _____

V. Complete each sentence below with the most appropriate word from the following vocabulary list:

Vocabulary List

tattered	morsel	prompted
affectionate	immaculate	rigid
repented	groped	terror
crouched	addressed	sensitive

1. Our neighbors are very neat; their home is always _____.

2. As Van was about to make his first jump, the thought that his parachute might not open filled him with _____.

3. This morning's forecast of heavy showers _____ Linda to take her umbrella.

4. Peggy noticed that the room was getting colder before I did; she is more _____ to changes in temperature.

5. This stick is too _____ for a bow; find one that bends more easily.

6. When Joe lost his temper, he made some remarks that he later _____.

7. One day Mother hid Dad's _____ wool muffler in the hope that he would buy himself a new one.

8. I _____ under the bed for my missing slipper, first with one hand and then with the other.

9. By the time Dean was ready for some cake, only a thin _____ was left.

10. A car whizzed by dangerously close to Chuck as he _____ to change a flat tire.

VI. On lines B and C, write the required forms of the italicized word on line A.

1. A. The nephew got an *affectionate* reception.

   B. The nephew was received _____.

   C. The nephew was greeted with _____.

2. A. Mary read the selection without *pausing*.

   B. Mary did not _____ at all in her reading.

C. Mary read the selection without a _____.

3. A. I was under *tension*.

   B. I waited _____.

   C. I was _____.

4. A. Did he *repent*?

   B. Was he _____?

   C. Did he show _____?

5. A. Weren't you *dazed* by the news?

   B. Didn't the news _____ you?

   C. Didn't the news leave you in a _____?

6. A. In a hospital, *immaculateness* is absolutely necessary.

   B. A hospital should be _____ maintained.

   C. A hospital must be _____.

7. A. Are the numbers in *serial* order?

   B. Are the numbers arranged in a _____.

   C. Are the numbers arranged _____?

8. A. Do you claim to be a *prophet*?

   B. Can you _____ who will win tomorrow?

   C. What is your _____ about the outcome of tomorrow's game?

9. A. She sat *mutely* as I asked question after question.

   B. She remained _____ to all my questions.

   C. She replied to my inquiries with absolute _____.

10. A. Paul prepares his work with *earnestness*.

   B. Paul does his work _____.

   C. Paul is an _____ student.

11. A. The Puritans had a reputation for *soberness*.

   B. They were _____ dressed.

   C. In their _____ way of life, there was no place for dancing and merrymaking.

12. A. The umpire *rigidly* clung to his decision.

B. The umpire was ＿＿＿＿＿＿ in sticking to his decision.

C. The umpire adhered to his decision with ＿＿＿＿＿＿＿.

13. A. Disease may make a person *deformed*.

B. Disease may cause a ＿＿＿＿＿＿＿＿.

C. Disease may ＿＿＿＿＿＿ a person's body.

14. A. Do you always speak in a *whining* voice?

B. Do you always speak with a ＿＿＿＿＿?

C. Do you always ＿＿＿＿＿?

15. A. We must not allow *terrorism*.

B. We will not permit criminals to strike ＿＿＿＿＿＿ into the hearts of peaceful citizens.

C. We must not allow criminals to ＿＿＿＿＿＿＿ peaceful citizens.

16. A. Alice has a *sensitive* ear for music.

B. Alice listens to music ＿＿＿＿＿＿＿＿.

C. Alice has a ＿＿＿＿＿＿＿＿ to good music.

17. A. Have you noticed that the child is *withdrawn*?

B. Have you noticed that the child tends to ＿＿＿＿＿＿＿ from others?

C. Have you noticed the child's ＿＿＿＿＿＿＿ from group activities?

18. A. Are you *positive* that you saw him there?

B. Did you ＿＿＿＿＿＿＿＿ see him there?

C. Can you say with ＿＿＿＿＿＿＿ that you saw him there?

19. A. You have failed in the *discharge* of your duties.

B. You left without ＿＿＿＿＿＿＿＿＿ your duties.

C. You did not ＿＿＿＿＿＿ your duties.

20. A. Wasn't the lightning *terrifying*?

B. Weren't you ＿＿＿＿＿＿＿ by the lightning?

C. Didn't the lightning ＿＿＿＿＿＿＿ you?

GROUP III / Reading Selections 9–12

READING SELECTION 9

*Richard Henry Dana, Jr. was a seaman aboard the Pilgrim in
1835, when the following true incident occurred. The captain was
about to whip Sam, a sailor with whom he had had an argument,
when another seaman, John, the Swede, asked a question.*

from

Two Years Before the Mast

by Richard Henry Dana, Jr.

"What are you going to flog that man for, sir?" said John, the
Swede, to the captain.

Upon hearing this, the captain turned upon John; but, knowing
him to be quick and resolute, he ordered the steward to bring the
5 irons, and, calling upon Russell to help him, went up to John.

"Let me alone," said John. "I'm willing to be put in irons. You
need not use any force"; and, putting out his hands, the captain
slipped the irons on, and set him aft to the quarter-deck. Sam, by
this time, was *seized up*, as it is called; that is, placed against the
10 shrouds, with his wrists made fast to them, his jacket off, and his
back exposed. The captain stood on the break of the deck, a few
feet from him, and a little raised, so as to have a good swing at
him, and held in his hand the end of a thick, strong rope. The
officers stood round, and the crew grouped together in the waist.
15 All these preparations made me feel sick and almost faint, angry
and excited as I was. A man—a human being, made in God's like-
ness—fastened up and flogged like a beast! A man, too, whom I
had lived with, eaten with, and stood watch with for months, and
knew so well!

20 The first impulse was to resist—but what was to be done?
Two men were fast, and there were left only two men besides

Stimson and myself, and a small boy of ten or twelve years of age; and Stimson and I would not have joined the men in a mutiny, as they knew. And then, on the other side, there were (besides the captain) three officers, steward, agent, and clerk, and the cabin supplied with weapons. But besides the numbers, what is there for sailors to do? If they resist, it is mutiny; and if they succeed, and take the vessel, it is piracy. If they ever yield again, their punishment must come; and if they do not yield, what are they to be for the rest of their lives? If a sailor resist his commander, he resists the law, and piracy or submission is his only alternative. Bad as it was, they saw it must be borne. It is what a sailor ships for. Swinging the rope over his head, and bending his body so as to give it full force, the captain brought it down upon the poor fellow's back. Once, twice,—six times. "Will you ever give me any more of your jaw?" The man writhed with pain, but said not a word. Three times more. This was too much, and he muttered something which I could not hear; this brought as many more as the man could stand, when the captain ordered him to be cut down.

"Now for you," said the captain, making up to John, and taking his irons off. As soon as John was loose, he ran forward to the forecastle. "Bring that man aft!" shouted the captain. The second mate, who had been in the forecastle with these men the early part of the voyage, stood still in the waist, and the mate walked slowly forward; but our third officer, anxious to show his zeal, sprang forward over the windlass, and laid hold of John; but John soon threw him from him. The captain stood on the quarter-deck, bareheaded, his eyes flashing with rage, and his face as red as blood, swinging the rope, and calling out to his officers, "Drag him aft! Lay hold of him! I'll *sweeten him!*" etc., etc. The mate now went forward, and told John quietly to go aft; and he, seeing resistance vain, threw the blackguard third mate from him, said he would go aft of himself, that they should not drag him, and went up to the gangway and held out his hands; but as soon as the captain began to make him fast, the indignity was too much, and he struggled; but, the mate and Russell holding him, he was soon seized up. When he was made fast, he turned to the captain, who stood rolling up his sleeves, getting ready for the blow, and asked him what he was to be flogged for. "Have I ever refused my duty, sir? Have you ever known me to hang back or to be insolent, or not to know my work?"

"No," said the captain, "it is not that that I flog you for; I flog you for your interference, for asking questions."

"Can't a man ask a question here without being flogged?"

"No," shouted the captain; "nobody shall open his mouth aboard this vessel but myself"; and he began laying the blows upon his back, swinging half round between each blow, to give it full effect. As he went on his passion increased, and he danced about the deck, calling out, as he swung the rope, "If you want to know what I flog you for, I'll tell you. It's because I like to do it! because I like to do it! It suits me! That's what I do it for!"

Understanding What You Have Read

In the blank space write the *letter* of the choice that best completes the statement or answers the question.

1. The one who shows himself most lacking in self-control is ____.

   A. the captain
   B. John
   C. Sam
   D. the narrator

2. John does not put up a struggle when ____.

   A. his irons are removed
   B. he is put in irons
   C. the captain orders him to be brought aft
   D. the third mate lays hold of him

3. Which of the following happens first? ____

   A. Sam is flogged.
   B. John is flogged.
   C. The third mate is thrown down.
   D. John is put in irons.

4. The narrator does not try to stop the flogging because he feels ____.

   A. it is none of his business
   B. the captain should always be obeyed
   C. all the odds are against him
   D. Sam and John should not have talked back

5. The passage indicates that ____.

   A. no sailor could be deprived of freedom of speech
   B. the captain was absolute master aboard his ship
   C. none of the mates wanted to obey the captain
   D. the courts would have pardoned the sailors if they had seized the ship

Learning New Words

Line	Word	Meaning	Typical Use
31	**alternative** (n.) ȯl-'tər-nət-iv	choice between two things; one of the two (or more) things from which a choice is to be made; choice	An election in which there is only one candidate is unfair to the voters because it does not give them an *alternative*.

116

20	**impulse** (*n.*) 'im-,pəls	sudden arousing of the mind and spirit to do something; sudden inclination to act; urge	When my paper was returned with a mark of 55, I had an almost uncontrollable *impulse* to tear it up.
55	**indignity** (*n.*) in-'dig-nət-ē	act that offends a person's dignity or self-respect; insult; outrage	The arrested man protested that he was innocent and that it was an *indignity* for him to be searched and fingerprinted.
60	**insolent** (*adj.*) 'in(t)-sə-lənt	boldly rude; disrespectful; insulting	Frank later realized that he had been *insolent* when he told his aunt that she didn't know what she was talking about.
		(*ant.* **courteous, respectful**)	The stranger who asked for directions was *courteous;* he thanked us for our help.
48	**rage** (*n.*) 'rāj	violent and uncontrollable anger; fury	In a *rage* over not getting his way, Dale overturned his chair and ran out of the house, slamming the front door.
20	**resist** (*v.*) ri-'zist	exert force in opposition; fight against; oppose	The surrounded suspect gave himself up when he saw that it would be futile to *resist.*
		(*ant.* **submit, yield**)	Instead of surrendering, the rebels swore that they would never *submit.*
31	**submission** (*n.*) səb-'mish-ən	act of *submitting* (giving in or surrendering) to the power or authority of another; obedience	The invaders expected quick *submission* from the inhabitants, but they met with fierce resistance.
		(*ant.* **resistance**)	When the detective approached, the suspect surrendered quietly, without offering any *resistance.*
36	**writhe** (*v.*) 'rīth	twist and turn this way and that; squirm	I couldn't sit still because my itching sunburn made me *writhe* in pain.
29	**yield** (*v.*) 'yēld	give up; cease resistance; surrender	The police called on the suspects to surrender but they refused to *yield.*
		(*ant.* **resist**)	

| 45 | zeal *(n.)*
'zēl | active enthusiastic interest;
eagerness; ardor; fervor | I used to do my piano practice
with *zeal;* now I have little en-
thusiasm for it. |
| | | *(ant.* **apathy***)* | If you were really interested in
the club, you would come to
meetings. By staying away, you
are showing your *apathy.* |

Applying What You Have Learned

I. Which of the two choices makes the sentence correct? Write the *letter* of the correct answer in the space provided.

1. A person in a rage is ____.

   A. in a good mood   B. likely to be violent

2. My zeal for the subject has led me to do ____ is required.

   A. much more than   B. less than

3. ____ if you stop writhing.

   A. People will think you are lazy   B. The barber may be able to cut your hair

4. It is an indignity to ____.

   A. have a door slammed in your face   B. be praised for your work

5. Should we resist or ____?

   A. continue the fight   B. give in

6. When someone is insolent to you, he ____.

   A. is showing disrespect   B. does not mean to hurt your feelings

7. People who buy on impulse ____.

   A. never use cash   B. give little thought to what they are buying

8. The enemy yielded and ____.

   A. laid down their arms   B. called on us to surrender

9. When you have no alternative, you have ____.

   A. very few choices   B. no choice

10. The bandits' submission came as a surprise. No one believed they would ever ____.

    A. give up   B. get away

II. The meaning of each expression below can be found in the vocabulary list at the bottom of the exercise. Find that meaning and write it in the space provided.

_____ **1.** fight against

_____ **2.** act that offends a person's self-respect

_____ **3.** violent and uncontrollable anger

_____ **4.** sudden inclination to act

_____ **5.** give up

_____ **6.** choice between two things

_____ **7.** act of giving in to the power of another

_____ **8.** active enthusiastic interest

_____ **9.** boldly rude

_____ **10.** twist and turn this way and that

Vocabulary List

impulse	insolent	yield	resist	writhe
submission	indignity	alternative	zeal	rage

III. Synonyms and Antonyms

A. Replace the italicized word with a _synonym_ from the vocabulary list on the next page.

_____ **1.** My itching sunburn made me _squirm._

_____ **2.** She was in a _fury._

_____ **3.** Do you have any _choice_?

_____ **4.** At that moment I had an _urge_ to walk out.

_____ **5.** Why does he think it an _outrage_ to have to work?

119

B. Replace the italicized word with an *antonym* from the vocabulary list.

_____ **6.** Their *resistance* came as no surprise.

_____ **7.** Marie's brother was extremely *courteous*.

_____ **8.** We thought they would not *resist*.

_____ **9.** Fred worked on his report with *apathy*.

_____ **10.** Circumstances compelled us to *submit*.

Vocabulary List

insolent	rage
indignity	yield
writhe	impulse
zeal	submission
resist	alternative

IV. Picture Quiz

In the blank space, write the *letter* of the picture that best fits the meaning of the sentence.

1. ____ is making a gesture of submission.

2. Waitress ____ offers an alternative.

3. A ____ usually writhes when it moves.

Learning Some Derivatives

Each word in bold type below is a *root*. The words below it are its *derivatives*.

Note that *alternate* is pronounced 'ȯl-tər-nət as an adjective, but 'ȯl-tər-ˌnāt as a verb.

alternate *(adj.)*
'ȯl-tər-nət

One way to get to the gym is by the elevator; an *alternaie* way is by the stairs.

alternate *(v.)*
'ȯl-tər-ˌnāt

My brother and I *alternate* in cleaning our room; he cleans up one week, and I the next.

alternately *(adv.)*
'ȯl-tər-nət-lē

We clean our room *alternately*.

alternative *(n.)*
ȯl-'tər-nət-iv

Since the elevator was not running, the only way for us to get to the gym was by the stairs; we had no *alternative*.

impulse *(n.)*	When Gordon thinks he knows the answer, he cannot resist the *impulse* to blurt it out.
impulsive *(adj.)*	Instead of being *impulsive,* Gordon should get permission before he speaks.
impulsively *(adv.)*	He is bound to be disliked if he continues to answer *impulsively*.
insolent *(adj.)*	You were *insolent* to my friend when you told her to mind her own business.
insolently *(adv.)*	She was not rude to you. Why did you speak so *insolently* to her?
insolence *(n.)*	You can accomplish more through courtesy than through *insolence*.
rage *(n.)*	When the dictator heard that his orders had not been carried out, he was in a *rage*.
rage *(v.)*	He *raged* like a madman.
resist *(v.)*	Proper rest, diet, and exercise will help you *resist* disease.
resistant *(adj.)*	A healthy body is usually *resistant* to disease.
resistance *(n.)*	Your physician can help you build up your *resistance*.
submit *(v.)*	The Boston patriots refused to *submit* to King George.
submissive *(adj.)*	They were not *submissive*.
submissively *(adv.)*	They would not *submissively* obey the commands of a foreign ruler.
submission *(n.)*	They refused to pay the tax on tea because to do so would have been an act of *submission*.
zeal *(n.)*	Martha is supporting me with remarkable *zeal;* she has persuaded several of her friends to vote for me.
zealous *(adj.)*	Martha is one of my most *zealous* supporters.
zealously *(adv.)*	Martha is *zealously* working for my election.

Fill each blank below with the word on the previous list that best fits the meaning of the sentence.

1. Don't _____ like a madman! Control your anger!

2. I guess I must have acted _____. I don't know what made me walk out.

3. Some _____ baseball fans travel to Florida to watch their favorite teams in spring exhibition games.

4. There was some construction work on the highway; therefore, we took (a)an _____ route.

5. The colt at first was not _____, throwing anyone who ventured to ride him.

6. Your rudeness to our visitors was unpardonable. We were deeply embarrassed by your _____.

7. An _____ person is one who acts on a sudden inclination, without bothering to think of the consequences.

8. Barbara, one of our very eager new members, acted as secretary, and she took the minutes _____.

9. The older boys were rude when we asked them for a chance to play; they _____ told us to "get lost."

10. Some of the rebels did not submit, but fled to the hills to continue their _____.

Improving Your Spelling:
Words Ending in -ANCE, -ENCE, -ANT, and -ENT

"... and he, seeing *resistance* vain ..."

"... I flog you for your *interference* ..."

1. Why do some nouns, like *resistance,* end in -ANCE, while others, like *interference,* end in -ENCE?

There is no simple rule to help with this problem. You must study each commonly used -ANCE and -ENCE noun separately, and consult the dictionary when in doubt. Here are some nouns to review.

-ANCE	-ENCE
abundance	adherence
allegiance	adolescence
appliance	affluence
assistance	audience
attendance	coherence
brilliance	confidence
compliance	correspondence
defiance	impatience
disturbance	incompetence
elegance	independence

endurance	indifference
extravagance	indolence
ignorance	indulgence
importance	insolence
observance	interference
perseverance	negligence
reliance	occurrence
repentance	permanence
resemblance	vehemence
resistance	violence

2. (A) Note that many nouns ending in -ANCE become adjectives ending in -ANT.

noun I G N O R A N C E becomes

adjective I G N O R A N T

(B) Certain -ANCE nouns, however, become adjectives by adding -ING, rather than -ANT.

noun E N D U R A N C E becomes

adjective E N D U R I N G

(C) Many nouns ending in -ENCE become adjectives ending in -ENT.

noun I N S O L E N C E becomes

adjective I N S O L E N T

I. Write the adjective form for each of the following nouns:

NOUN	ADJECTIVE
1. independence	_____
2. brilliance	_____
3. abundance	_____
4. vehemence	_____
5. disturbance	_____

6. repentance   _____

7. indolence   _____

8. perseverance   _____

9. coherence   _____

10. reliance   _____

II. Write the noun form for each of the following adjectives:

ADJECTIVE	NOUN
1. defiant	_____
2. extravagant	_____
3. indifferent	_____
4. indulgent	_____
5. enduring	_____
6. permanent	_____
7. confident	_____
8. assistant	_____
9. ignorant	_____
10. resembling	_____

III. Write the missing letter in column A and the complete word in column B.

Column A	Column B
1. repent __ nt	_____
2. compli __ nce	_____
3. indiffer __ nt	_____
4. adolesc __ nce	_____
5. self-confid __ nt	_____
6. persever __ nce	_____
7. incoher __ nt	_____
8. occurr __ nce	_____

9. appli __ nce   _____

10. eleg __ nt   _____

11. resist __ nce   _____

12. self-reli __ nt   _____

13. disturb __ nce   _____

14. vehem __ nt   _____

15. interfer __ nce   _____

16. unimport __ nt   _____

17. viol __ nce   _____

18. observ __ nt   _____

19. allegi __ nce   _____

20. adher __ nt   _____

Correct Usage: Punctuating Words of Direct Address

1. Words of *direct address* are words that tell us to whom a remark is being directed.

The italicized words below are words of direct address:

When are you leaving, *Jennifer*?

Bob, your breakfast is ready.

I am here today, *my fellow students*, to ask for your support.

2. Set off words of direct address from the rest of the sentence by commas.

Use *one* comma when words of direct address begin or end the sentence:

Linda, please mail these letters on your way to school.

Please mail these letters on your way to school, *Linda*.

Otherwise, use *two* commas:

Please mail these letters, *Linda*, on your way to school.

Rewrite each sentence, adding the necessary punctuation.

1. Wait for me Joe

   _____

2. What are you going to flog that man for sir

   _____

3. Dad this call is for you

   _____

4. Are you feeling better Jack

   _____

5. Listen my children and you shall hear

   _____

6. Norman please close the window

   _____

7. May I ask a question Mr. Carr

   _____

8. This ladies and gentlemen is our last chance

   _____

9. Pat is this yours

   _____

10. Have I ever refused my duty sir

   _____

In an emergency, do you lose your head, or do you remain calm enough to act intelligently?

The narrator, a fourteen-year-old boy living in the Texas hill country in the 1860's, describes an emergency in which he was involved.

from

Old Yeller

by Fred Gipson

That's when I heard Little Arliss scream.

Well, Little Arliss was a screamer by nature. He'd scream when he was happy and scream when he was mad and a lot of times he'd scream just to hear himself make a noise. Generally, we paid no
5 more mind to his screaming than we did to the gobble of a wild turkey.

But this time was different. The second I heard his screaming, I felt my heart flop clear over. This time I knew Little Arliss was in real trouble.

10 I tore out up the trail leading toward the cabin. A minute before, I'd been so tired out with my rail splitting that I couldn't have struck a trot. But now I raced through the tall trees in that creek bottom, covering ground like a scared wolf.

Little Arliss's second scream, when it came, was louder and
15 shriller and more frantic-sounding than the first. Mixed with it was a whimpering crying sound that I knew didn't come from him. It was a sound I'd heard before and seemed like I ought to know what it was, but right then I couldn't place it.

Then, from way off to one side came a sound that I would have
20 recognized anywhere. It was the coughing roar of a charging bear. I'd just heard it once in my life. That was the time Mama had shot and wounded a hog-killing bear and Papa had had to finish it off with a knife to keep it from getting her.

My heart went to pushing up into my throat, nearly choking off my wind. I strained for every lick of speed I could get out of my running legs. I didn't know what sort of fix Little Arliss had got himself into, but I knew that it had to do with a mad bear, which was enough.

The way the late sun slanted through the trees had the trail all cross-banded with streaks of bright light and dark shade. I ran through these bright and dark patches so fast that the changing light nearly blinded me. Then suddenly, I raced out into the open where I could see ahead. And what I saw sent a chill clear through to the marrow of my bones.

There was Little Arliss, down in that spring hole again. He was lying half in and half out of the water, holding onto the hind leg of a little black bear cub no bigger than a small coon. The bear cub was out on the bank, whimpering and crying and clawing the rocks with all three of his other feet, trying to pull away. But Little Arliss was holding on for all he was worth, scared now and screaming his head off. Too scared to let go.

How come the bear cub ever to prowl close enough for Little Arliss to grab him, I don't know. And why he didn't turn on him and bite loose, I couldn't figure out, either. Unless he was like Little Arliss, too scared to think.

But all of that didn't matter now. What mattered was the bear cub's mama. She'd heard the cries of her baby and was coming to save him. She was coming so fast that she had the brush popping and breaking as she crashed through and over it. I could see her black heavy figure piling off down the slant on the far side of Birdsong Creek. She was roaring mad and ready to kill.

And worst of all, I could see that I'd never get there in time!

Mama couldn't either. She'd heard Arliss, too, and here she came from the cabin, running down the slant toward the spring, screaming at Arliss, telling him to turn the bear cub loose. But Little Arliss wouldn't do it. All he'd do was hang with that hind leg and let out one shrill shriek after another as fast as he could suck in a breath.

Now the she bear was charging across the shallows in the creek. She was knocking sheets of water high in the bright sun, charging with her fur up and her long teeth bared, filling the canyon with that awful coughing roar. And no matter how fast Mama ran or how fast I ran, the she bear was going to get there first!

I think I nearly went blind then, picturing what was going to happen to Little Arliss. I know that I opened my mouth to scream and not any sound came out.

Then, just as the bear went lunging up the creek bank toward Little Arliss and her cub, a flash of yellow came streaking out of the brush.

It was that big yeller dog. He was roaring like a mad bull. He wasn't one-third as big and heavy as the she bear, but when he piled into her from one side, he rolled her clear off her feet. They

75 went down in a wild, roaring tangle of twisting bodies and scrambling feet and slashing fangs.

As I raced past them, I saw the bear lunge up to stand on her hind feet like a man while she clawed at the body of the yeller dog hanging to her throat. I didn't wait to see more. Without ever checking my stride, I ran in and jerked Little Arliss loose from
80 the cub. I grabbed him by the wrist and yanked him up out of that water and slung him toward Mama like he was a half-empty sack of corn. I screamed at Mama. "Grab him, Mama! Grab him and run!" Then I swung my chopping axe high and wheeled, aiming to cave in the she bear's head with the first lick.

Line 37. *coon:* raccoon

Understanding What You Have Read

In the blank space, write the *letter* of the choice that best completes the statement.

1. The whimpering and crying sound came from ＿＿.

   A. Little Arliss
   B. a mad she bear
   C. a bear cub
   D. a raccoon

2. According to the narrator, Arliss kept holding on to the cub because ＿＿.

   A. he was frightened
   B. he didn't want it to escape
   C. it had a grip on him
   D. he didn't want it to bite him

3. The passage compares ＿＿ to a mad bull.

   A. Arliss
   B. the bear
   C. the bear cub
   D. the yellow dog

4. The main incident described in the passage occurred at about ＿＿.

   A. noon
   B. 5 P.M.
   C. 11 A.M.
   D. 8 A.M.

5. The passage suggests that ＿＿.

   A. bear cubs are harmless
   B. Papa is not at home
   C. Mama handles a rifle expertly
   D. there is little game in the area

Learning New Words

Line	Word	Meaning	Typical Use
70	**brush** (n.) 'brəsh	thick growth of bushes, shrubs, and small trees; brushwood; scrub	The forest rangers had to cut their way through the *brush* to reach the scene of the crash.
79	**check** (v.) 'chek	bring to a sudden halt; stop; restrain; curb	Decay in a tooth must be *checked* as soon as it is discovered.
37	**cub** (n.) 'kəb	1. young bear, lion, or fox	The lioness and her mate take care of their *cubs* until they can fend for themselves.
		2. apprentice, especially an inexperienced newspaper reporter; novice; beginner	Students without previous experience are assigned as *cubs* when they join the staff of the school newspaper.
75	**fang** (n.) 'faŋ	long, sharp, pointed tooth by which an animal's prey is seized and held or torn; tooth	Anyone whose skin is pierced by the *fangs* of a poisonous snake must receive first aid immediately.
15	**frantic** (adj.) 'frant-ik	wildly or uncontrollably excited; frenzied	The *frantic* woman would have leaped from her window if the fireman had not reached her in time.
4	**generally** (adv.) 'jen-(ə-)rə-lē	usually; as a rule; in most cases	*Generally,* my sister picks up the phone when it rings, but this time I got to it first.
76	**lunge** (v.) 'lənj	make a forceful forward movement; plunge	One of our men *lunged* at the swift ball carrier but failed to tackle him.
34	**marrow** (n.) 'mar-ō	soft tissue that fills the cavities of most bones; inmost, best, or essential part	It was so cold in the room that I was chilled to the *marrow* of my bones.
42	**prowl** (v.) 'praůl	move about slowly and stealthily like a wild beast seeking prey; lurk; roam in search of whatever may be found	The residents feared that the escaped tiger might be *prowling* near their homes.
16	**whimper** (v.) 'hwim-pər	cry with low, complaining, broken sounds; whine	The child did not cry loudly but *whimpered* for nearly half an hour until she was given back her doll.

131

Applying What You Have Learned

I. Which of the two choices makes the sentence correct? Write the *letter* of the correct answer in the space provided.

1. Were you frantic when you were in danger or did you ____?

   A. get excited   B. remain calm

2. When the instructor says "Lunge," he wants everyone to ____ .

   A. move forward forcefully B. step aside gently

3. Visitors to the zoo often pay more attention to the cubs than to the ____ animals.

   A. younger   B. older

4. We must check the Red Sox rally to ____ .

   A. see if errors were made B. prevent further scoring

5. When the lion bared his fangs, I could see what sharp ____ he has.

   A. claws   B. teeth

6. Stop whimpering. You have nothing to ____ about.

   A. cry   B. brag

7. A ____ would have little trouble getting through the brush.

   A. wagon   B. snake

8. Inside the ____ is a substance called the marrow.

   A. bone   B. branch

9. Stan is generally on time; he is ____ late.

   A. never   B. seldom

10. If you see someone prowling in the neighborhood, it may be ____ .

    A. a burglar   B. the postman

II. The meaning of each expression below can be found in the vocabulary list on the next page. Find that meaning and write it in the space provided.

_____ 1. wildly or uncontrollably excited

_____ 2. make a forceful forward movement

_____ 3. long, sharp, pointed tooth

_____ 4. cry with low, complaining, broken sounds

_____ 5. as a rule

_____ 6. young bear, lion, or fox

_____ 7. soft tissue that fills bone cavities

_____ 8. move about slowly and stealthily

_____ 9. bring to a sudden halt

_____ 10. thick growth of bushes, shrubs, and small trees

Vocabulary List

whimper	prowl
marrow	frantic
brush	check
lunge	fang
generally	cub

III. Synonyms

In the space before each word or expression in column A, write its synonym selected from column B.

Column A   *Column B*

_____ 1. frenzied   cub

_____ 2. whine   lunge

_____ 3. usually   check

_____ 4. novice   whimper

_____ 5. inmost part   prowl

_____ 6. scrub   marrow

_____ 7. stop   frantic

_____ 8. tooth   brush

_____ 9. plunge   fang

_____ 10. lurk   generally

IV. Picture Quiz

In the blank space, write the *letter* of the picture that best fits the meaning of the sentence.

1. There is marrow in ____ .

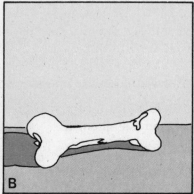

2. ____ cannot lunge.

3. ____ is getting frantic.

134

Learning Some Derivatives

Each word in bold type below is a *root*. The words below it are its *derivatives*.

brush *(n.)* — It is much easier to spot a golf ball in the short grass than one that has rolled into the *brush*.

brushwood *(n.)* — We have enough logs for the fire, but we could use some pieces of *brushwood* for kindling.

check *(v.)* — A way must be found to *check* unemployment.

check *(n.)* — A road building program will create jobs and serve as a *check* to unemployment.

unchecked *(adj.)* — Unemployment must not be permitted to continue *unchecked*.

frantic *(adj.)* — As I approached the water, I heard a *frantic* cry for help.

frantically *(adv.)* — Someone whose boat had overturned was shouting *frantically* for help.

general *(adj.)* — The dean's *general* practice is to notify your parents if you get into trouble.

generally *(adv.)* — *Generally*, the dean will notify your parents if you get into trouble.

lunge *(v.)* — Jackson *lunged* at me with a powerful right, but missed.

lunge *(n.)* — Luckily, I avoided Jackson's *lunge*.

marrow *(n.)* — The bones of our arms and legs are filled with *marrow*.

marrowy *(adj.)* — Red blood cells are produced in the *marrowy* tissues of our bones.

prowl *(v.)* — Stray cats *prowl* the streets at night.

prowl *(n.)* — Our garbage can was knocked over by a stray dog on the *prowl*.

prowler *(n.)* — The neighbor's cat stays indoors; he is no *prowler*.

whimper *(v.)* — Mother got up when she heard the baby *whimper*.

whimper *(n.)* — Mother was awakened by the baby's *whimper*.

Fill each blank with the word listed above that best fits the meaning of the sentence.

1. Our neighbor called the police at 2 A.M. when he thought he saw a(an)

_____ in the back yard.

2. Alex, who was uncontrollably excited by the decision, argued with the umpires so _____ that he was thrown out of the game.

3. Mother says that _____ bones are good for soup.

4. We will be able to make quicker progress once we get out of the _____ and into the open fields.

5. For years we permitted our air and water to be polluted without even a(an) _____ of protest.

6. *Theater* is now the _____ spelling; *theatre* is becoming more and more rare.

7. When a fencer makes a(an) _____ at his opponent, he suddenly extends his right arm and advances his right foot as far as possible.

8. If a forest fire is allowed to rage _____, it will spread very rapidly.

9. Two detectives followed the suspect as he began his nightly _____.

10. The Supreme Court exercises a(an) _____ on the misuse of power by legislators when it declares a law unconstitutional.

Improving Your Spelling: One Hundred Demons

The passage we have just read from OLD YELLER contains a large number of the words appearing in the famous list of *One Hundred Spelling Demons* below. These words are so often used that everyone should be able to spell them with complete accuracy. Review the list. Then do the exercise that follows.

One Hundred Spelling Demons

ache	built	dear	friend
again	business	doctor	grammar
always	busy	does	guess
among	buy	done	half
answer	can't	don't	having
any	choose	early	hear
been	color	easy	heard
beginning	coming	enough	here
believe	cough	every	hoarse
blue	could	February	hour
break	country	forty	instead

just	piece	tear	very
knew	raise	their	wear
know	read	there	Wednesday
laid	ready	they	week
loose	said	though	where
lose	says	through	whether
making	seems	tired	which
many	separate	tonight	whole
meant	shoes	too	women
minute	since	trouble	won't
much	some	truly	would
none	straight	Tuesday	write
often	sugar	two	writing
once	sure	used	wrote

Each sentence below contains three words with missing letters.
Fill in the missing letters. (Each space stands for one letter.) Then
write the complete word.

1. T __ __ p __ __ ces of pie should be en __ __ gh.

_____   _____   _____

2. I bel __ __ ve the ans __ __ r is f __ rty-four.

_____   _____   _____

3. My fr __ __ nd Pat has no tr __ __ ble with her gramm __ r.

_____   _____   _____

4. Many w __ men w __ __ r high-heeled sh __ __ s.

_____   _____   _____

5. My throat is h __ __ rse, Doct __ r, and I have a bad c __ __ gh.

_____   _____   _____

6. She s __ __ d she'd be r __ __ dy in a min __ __ __.

_____   _____   _____

7. It snowed the last T __ __ sday and We __ __ __ sday in Feb __ __ ary.

_____   _____   _____

8. In the c __ __ ntry, the leaves are beg __ __ __ ing to change c __ l __ r.

_____   _____   _____

9. Noisy sanitation trucks rumble **thr __ __ gh** town at an __ __ **rly h __ __ r.**

_____   _____   _____

10. Ask the waiter **w __ __ ther** he can seat us together, **inst __ __ d** of **sep __ rately.**

_____   _____   _____

Grammar: The Present Participle

1. To form the present participle of a verb, add *ing:*

> whimper + ing = whimpering
> charge + ing = charging
> run   + ing = running

2. Use the present participle to avoid repetition and to make your sentences more grown-up and more interesting.

Compare the following two descriptions.

Description A – Present Participle Not Used

BABYISH
> She came from the cabin. She ran down the slant toward the spring. She screamed at Arliss. She told him to turn the bear cub loose.

Description B – Present Participle Used

MATURE
> She came from the cabin, *running* down the slant toward the spring, *screaming* at Arliss, *telling* him to turn the bear cub loose.

Note how the use of the present participles *running, screaming,* and *telling* in Description B enables the writer to:

> avoid unnecessary repetition of the subject. In Description A, the subject *She* is used four times, but in Description B only once.

> replace the four "baby" sentences in Description A with one grown-up sentence.

> make the description more exciting and interesting.

3. Use a comma to set off the participial phrase from the rest of the sentence.

I left the room , taking my books.

Taking my books , I left the room.

138

Change each group of sentences below to one sentence by using present participles.

SAMPLE: They passed us quickly. They looked angry.
They passed us quickly, looking angry.

1. We talked for a while. We exchanged ideas.

   _____

2. Fred drove by on his motorbike. He waved to his friends.

   _____

3. I raced through the tall trees in that creek bottom. I covered ground like a scared wolf.

   _____

   _____

4. The river overflowed. It flooded streets and basements.

   _____

5. The bear cub was out on the bank. He whimpered. He cried. He clawed the rocks. He tried to pull away.

   _____

   _____

6. A lady with a tall hat sat directly in front of me. She blocked my view.

   _____

   _____

7. He was lying half in and half out of the water. He was holding on to the hind leg of a little black bear cub.

   _____

   _____

8. They started at 8 A.M. They hoped to finish by noon.

   _____

*The following takes place in the center of a railroad bridge over a
stream in Northern Alabama during the Civil War.*

from

An Occurrence at Owl Creek Bridge

by Ambrose Bierce

The man who was engaged in being hanged was apparently
about thirty-five years of age. He was a civilian, if one might judge
from his habit, which was that of a planter. His features were
good—a straight nose, firm mouth, broad forehead, from which
5 his long, dark hair was combed straight back, falling behind his
ears to the collar of his well-fitting frock coat. He wore a mustache
and pointed beard, but no whiskers; his eyes were large and dark
gray, and had a kindly expression which one would hardly have
expected in one whose neck was in the hemp. Evidently this was
10 no vulgar assassin. The liberal military code makes provision
for hanging many kinds of persons, and gentlemen are not
excluded.

The preparations being complete, the two private soldiers
stepped aside and each drew away the plank upon which he had
15 been standing. The sergeant turned to the captain, saluted and
placed himself immediately behind that officer, who in turn moved
apart one pace. These movements left the condemned man and
the sergeant standing on the two ends of the same plank, which
spanned three of the cross-ties of the bridge. The end upon which
20 the civilian stood almost, but not quite, reached a fourth. This
plank had been held in place by the weight of the captain; it was
now held by that of the sergeant. At a signal from the former the
latter would step aside, the plank would tilt and the condemned

man go down between two ties. The arrangement commended
itself to his judgment as simple and effective. His face had not 25
been covered nor his eyes bandaged. He looked a moment at his
"unsteadfast footing," then let his gaze wander to the swirling
water of the stream racing madly beneath his feet. A piece of
dancing driftwood caught his attention and his eyes followed it
down the current. How slowly it appeared to move! What a 30
sluggish stream!

He closed his eyes in order to fix his last thoughts upon his
wife and children. The water, touched to gold by the early sun, the
brooding mists under the banks at some distance down the stream,
the fort, the soldiers, the piece of drift—all had distracted him. 35
And now he became conscious of a new disturbance. Striking
through the thought of his dear ones was a sound which he could
neither ignore nor understand, a sharp, distinct, metallic percus-
sion like the stroke of a blacksmith's hammer upon the anvil; it
had the same ringing quality. He wondered what it was, and 40
whether immeasurably distant or near by—it seemed both. Its
recurrence was regular, but as slow as the tolling of a death knell.
He waited each stroke with impatience and—he knew not why—
apprehension. The intervals of silence grew progressively longer;
the delays became maddening. With their greater infrequency the 45
sounds increased in strength and sharpness. They hurt his ear
like the thrust of a knife; he feared he would shriek. What he
heard was the ticking of his watch.

He unclosed his eyes and saw again the water below him. "If I
could free my hands," he thought, "I might throw off the noose 50
and spring into the stream. By diving I could evade the bullets
and, swimming vigorously, reach the bank, take to the woods and
get away home. My home, thank God, is as yet outside their lines;
my wife and little ones are still beyond the invader's farthest
advance." 55

Line 19. *cross-ties:* timbers across which railroad rails are fastened

Understanding What You Have Read

In the blank space, write the *letter* of the choice that best completes the statement.

1. The action described in the passage takes place _____.

    A. before sunrise
    B. at sundown
    C. in the early morning
    D. in the late afternoon

2. The plank on which the condemned man is standing is being held in place by _____.

    A. three cross-ties

B. the weight of two private soldiers
C. two other planks
D. the weight of the sergeant

3. The passage suggests that _____.

   A. there is a fort nearby
   B. the condemned man's hands are loosely tied
   C. there are no armed soldiers at the scene
   D. the condemned man is a common criminal

4. The condemned man _____.

   A. imagines that time is slipping away altogether too rapidly
   B. has given up all hope of escape
   C. does not understand that his watch is making unbearably painful sounds
   D. imagines that his home has been destroyed by the enemy

5. The author is mainly concerned with describing _____.

   A. the setting
   B. what is happening in the mind of the condemned man
   C. the thoughts of the officers and soldiers
   D. the appearance of the condemned man

Learning New Words

Line	Word	Meaning	Typical Use
1	**apparently** (adv.) ə-'par-ənt-lē	1. in an *apparent* (plain to see or visible) manner; evidently; obviously	Alan is *apparently* angry with me, as he hasn't said anything to me in a long time.
		2. seemingly (but not necessarily really) (*ant.* **really**)	The *apparently* worthless nag that Billy Dawes led past the British guards was one of the fastest horses in Boston.
44	**apprehension** (n.) ‚ap-ri-'hen-chən	fear of what may be coming; dread	Since I had reviewed my notes carefully, I took the test without *apprehension*.
		(*ant.* **confidence**)	As I was well prepared, I took the test with a feeling of *confidence*.
35	**distract** (v.) dis-'trakt	draw away (the attention or mind) to a different subject; divert	While the bus is in motion, do not do or say anything to *distract* the driver's attention.

51	**evade** *(v.)* i-'vād	1. get away from or avoid by skill or cleverness; elude	The candidate *evaded* the reporters by slipping out through a back door.
		2. avoid facing up to	Answer truthfully; do not attempt to *evade* the question.
12	**exclude** *(v.)* iks-'klüd	shut out; keep out; bar from participation or inclusion	The security force is under instructions to *exclude* anyone who cannot show proper identification.
		(ant. **admit***)*	If an employee is not wearing his identification badge, the guard at the gate will not *admit* him.
		(ant. **include***)*	The price *includes* postage and shipping, but not local sales taxes.
22	**former** *(adj.)* 'fȯr-mər	coming before in time; earlier; previous; prior	Ralph feels better; he is beginning to recover his *former* strength.
	(n.)	first of two *(ant.* **latter***)*	Ralph and Bob are fine athletes. The *former* is our best pitcher. The *latter* is on the track team.
38	**ignore** *(v.)* ig-'nō(ə)r	refuse to take notice of; disregard	The accident occurred when one of the drivers *ignored* a red light.
		(ant. **heed***)*	If he had *heeded* the traffic signal, the accident would have been prevented.
23	**latter** *(adj.)* 'lat-ər	more recent; later	We are living in the *latter* half of the twentieth century.
	(n.)	second of two *(ant.* **former***)*	Both Lincoln and Washington were born in February—the *former* on the twelfth, and the *latter* on the twenty-second.
42	**recurrence** *(n.)* ri-'kər-ən(t)s	act of *recurring* (occurring or happening again); repetition	Mr. Ritchie told me he had ignored my former latenesses but would notify the dean at the next *recurrence*.
23	**tilt** *(v.)* 'tilt	cause to slope; incline; tip; slant	Since both teams are evenly matched, an injury to one of our key players can *tilt* the scales in favor of our opponents.

Applying What You Have Learned

I. Which of the two choices makes the sentence correct? Write the *letter* of the correct answer in the space provided.

1. You can go west by rail or by air, but the latter is usually ____.

   A. slower   B. faster

2. They tried to get ____, but they were excluded.

   A. out   B. in

3. Alice ignored us; she ____.

   A. asked us a great number of questions   B. pretended that we didn't even exist

4. If you sit ____ of that long bench, it may tilt.

   A. at the end   B. in the middle

5. A painting described as an apparently original Picasso ____.

   A. is definitely the work of that artist   B. may be an imitation

6. I ____ of the announcement because Sam distracted me.

   A. did not miss a single word   B. missed part

7. Both Alaska and Rhode Island are states, though the former is much ____.

   A. smaller   B. larger

8. ____ his first failure in spelling, Stan assured his parents that there would be no recurrence.

   A. Before   B. After

9. Our puppy ran ____ the postman, as if to evade him.

   A. after   B. away from

10. My aunt expressed apprehension about the trip because ____.

    A. she needed a vacation   B. the roads were slippery

II. The meaning of each expression below can be found in the vocabulary list at the bottom of the exercise. Find that meaning and write it in the space provided.

_____ 1. draw away the attention

_____ 2. act of happening again

_____ 3. keep out

144

_____ 4. second of two

_____ 5. fear of what may be coming

_____ 6. refuse to take notice of

_____ 7. cause to slope

_____ 8. in a plain-to-see manner

_____ 9. avoid by skill or cleverness

_____ 10. first of two

Vocabulary List

latter	distract
apprehension	evade
recurrence	ignore
former	tilt
apparently	exclude

III. Synonyms and Antonyms

A. Replace the italicized word with a *synonym* from the vocabulary list at the bottom of the exercise.

_____ 1. Mike tried to *elude* us.

_____ 2. There may be a *repetition* of last year's power failure.

_____ 3. How can I do my work if you *divert* my attention?

_____ 4. Don't *tip* the boat!

_____ 5. Dan hoped for a return of his *previous* good luck.

B. Replace the italicized word with an *antonym* from the vocabulary list.

_____ 6. I am sure they will *admit* us.

_____ 7. In all probability, George will *heed* the warning.

_____ 8. They chose the *former* of the two alternatives.

_____ 9. She undertook the assignment with *confidence*.

_____ 10. The magician *really* swallowed a sword.

Vocabulary List

distract	apparently
ignore	evade
former	latter
apprehension	tilt
recurrence	exclude

IV. Picture Quiz

In the blank space, write the *letter* of the picture that best fits the meaning of the sentence.

1. _____ is a sign that is intended to exclude.

2. The umbrella in _____ is tilted.

3. ____ is full of apprehension.

Learning Some Derivatives

Each word in bold type below is a *root*. The words below it are its *derivatives*.

apparent *(adj.)*	Your smile makes it *apparent* that you are pleased with your mark.
apparently *(adv.)*	*Apparently* you are pleased with your mark.
apprehend *(v.)*	There is no need to *apprehend* the outcome since everything will turn out all right.
apprehensive *(adj.)*	There is no reason to be *apprehensive*.
apprehensively *(adv.)*	Why do you look to the future *apprehensively*?
apprehension *(n.)*	Don't be afraid. I assure you that there is no cause for *apprehension*.
distract *(v.)*	I tried to study, but the loud playing of my neighbor's hi-fi *distracted* me.
distraction *(n.)*	Mother keeps the TV very low when I study to prevent it from being a *distraction*.
evade *(v.)*	The suspect *evaded* several questions by answering, "I can't remember."
evasive *(adj.)*	He gave *evasive* replies.
evasively *(adv.)*	He answered *evasively*.
evasion *(n.)*	He practiced *evasion*.
exclude *(v.)*	Tracy's Supermart has the right to *exclude* the cars of non-customers from its private parking lot.

147

exclusive *(adj.)*	The Tracy lot is for the *exclusive* use of Tracy shoppers.
exclusively *(adv.)*	Tracy's operates a parking field *exclusively* for its own patrons.
exclusion *(n.)*	If not for the *exclusion* of the general public, Tracy's clients would be unable to park in Tracy's lot.
former *(adj.)*	I returned to my *former* school in the country for a brief visit.
former *(n.)*	If I had to choose between a large city school and a small country school, I would pick the *former*.
formerly *(adv.)*	However, I would miss the friends that I had in the school I *formerly* attended.
latter *(adj.)*	In his previous appearances, the actor was unnoticed, but in *latter* roles he has won much praise.
latter *(n.)*	He prefers small parts. If offered a choice between the leading role and a minor part, he would select the *latter*.
latterly *(adv.)*	*Latterly,* the actor has become quite a star.
recur *(v.)*	Certain districts are plagued by floods that *recur* every spring.
recurrent *(adj.)*	The residents are annoyed by the *recurrent* floods.
recurrence *(n.)*	After each severe flood, they talk about what needs to be done to prevent a *recurrence*.
tilt *(v.)*	In going out, I brushed against the wall mirror, causing it to *tilt* slightly.
tilt *(n.)*	By moving the right side of the mirror up slightly, I corrected the *tilt*.

Fill each blank below with the word in the previous list that best fits the meaning of the sentence.

1. The pain is gone now, and I hope it will not _____.

2. From the way traffic was moving, it was _____ that our bus would not get to school on time.

3. The police have twice spotted their suspect in midtown but could not catch up with him; he is remarkably _____.

4. Coats that were _____ $150 are now on sale for $79.

5. The party is _____ for members of the Spanish Club; no one else will be invited.

6. There is a slight _____ in the furniture on one side of the room where the floor is uneven.

7. Mother became _____ when she heard the baby's cough, and she immediately called the doctor.

8. The teacher scolded Gary for making faces and creating a _____ that prevented the rest of the class from learning.

9. Since last March there have been _____ power failures in our neighborhood, about one every two weeks.

10. All classes must leave the gym floor by 3 o'clock. Their _____ is necessary so that our teams may practice.

Improving Your Spelling: Adding Suffixes to Words of More Than One Syllable

You will find a world of difference between "An Occurrence at Owl Creek Bridge" and the ordinary short story.

In the above sentence, why is the R in occuR doubled (occuRRence) when -ENCE is added, whereas the R in diffeR is not doubled (diffeRence)?

Here is the explanation:

A. In a word of two or more syllables, we double the final consonant if it is in an *accented* (stressed) syllable before a suffix beginning with a vowel.

WORD	SUFFIXES	NEW WORDS
oc′CUR	+ ed, ing, ence	= occuRRed, occuRRing, occuRRence
de′FER	+ ed, ing, al	= defeRRed, defeRRing, defeRRal

B. If the final consonant is in an *unaccented* syllable, do not double the final consonant.

′DIFfer	+ ed, ing, ence	= diffeRed, diffeRing, diffeRence
′BENefit	+ ed, ing	= benefiTed, benefiTing

Now that you have learned about occuRRence and diffeRence, you should study the following also:

C. Do not double the final consonant in these cases:

(1) if it comes right after another consonant.

condu⎡c⎤T   +   ed, ing, or   =   conducTed, conducTing, conducTor

recomme⎡n⎤D   +   ed, ing   =   recommenDed, recommenDing

(2) if it comes right after two vowels.

cont⎡ai⎤N   +   ed, ing, er   =   contaiNed, contaiNing, contaiNer

rep⎡ea⎤L   +   ed, ing   =   repeaLed, repeaLing

(3) if the accent shifts back to the first syllable.

con'FER   +   ence   =   'CONference
de'FER   +   ence   =   'DEFerence
pre'FER   +   ence   =   'PREFerence
re'FER   +   ence   =   'REFerence

However: ex'CEL + ence = 'EXcellence.

I. Write the new word.

WORD	SUFFIX		NEW WORD
1. recur	+ ence	=	_____
2. confer	+ ing	=	_____
3. obtain	+ ed	=	_____
4. propel	+ er	=	_____
5. label	+ ed	=	_____
6. regret	+ able	=	_____
7. conceal	+ ing	=	_____
8. occur	+ ed	=	_____
9. benefit	+ ing	=	_____
10. profit	+ able	=	_____
11. enter	+ ed	=	_____
12. recur	+ ence	=	_____

13. compel   + ed   = _____

14. commend + able = _____

15. permit   + ed   = _____

16. excel   + ence = _____

17. offer   + ed   = _____

18. appeal   + ing   = _____

19. differ   + ent   = _____

20. recur   + ent   = _____

II. For each word at the left, form the three derivatives indicated.

1. commend _____ed   _____ing   _____able

2. commit   _____ed   _____ing   _____ment

3. occur   _____ed   _____ing   _____ence

4. prefer   _____ed   _____ing   _____ence

5. regret   _____ed   _____ing   _____able

6. suffer   _____ed   _____ing   _____ance

7. extract _____ed   _____ing   _____ion

8. open   _____ed   _____ing   _____er

9. defer   _____ed   _____ing   _____ment

10. excel   _____ed   _____ing   _____ence

Correct Usage: Avoiding Unnecessary Words

A good writer avoids unnecessary words. Ambrose Bierce writes:

> "These movements left the condemned man and the sergeant standing on the two ends of the same plank, which spanned three of the cross-ties of the bridge. The end upon which the civilian stood almost, but not quite, reached a fourth."

We do not have to ask what the author means by "a fourth." From the previous sentence, we know that he means *a fourth cross-tie*.

In his next sentence, too, the author avoids unnecessary words:

"This plank had been held in place by the weight of the captain; it was now held (he does not repeat *in place*) by that (he does not repeat *the weight*) of the sergeant."

Following the example of Ambrose Bierce, you, too, should remove from your writing any words that repeat an idea already expressed. Note the following:

QUESTION: Our new gym is the *(finest gym, finest)* in town.
ANSWER: Our new gym is the *finest* in town.
EXPLANATION: Since *gym* is mentioned earlier in the sentence, to repeat it is unnecessary.

QUESTION: I didn't hear your answer; please *(repeat it, repeat it again)*.
ANSWER: I didn't hear your answer; please *repeat it*.
EXPLANATION: The word *again* is unnecessary because *repeat* means "say *again*."

Rewrite the following sentences, leaving out the unnecessary words.

1. My assignment is completely different from Jane's assignment.

_____

2. We will wait until we learn the true facts.

_____

3. The modern housewife of today uses many appliances.

_____

4. I have one glove but can't find the other one.

_____

5. A girl of about eight years old answered the telephone.

_____

6. The class has finished the first six chapters and is now working on the seventh chapter.

_____

7. On her head she wore a red and white skating cap.

_____

8. In my opinion, I believe you are right.

_____

Frederick Douglass, a slave, escaped to the North in 1838, when he was 21, and quickly became a leader in the struggle to abolish slavery. The following passage deals with his boyhood.

from

Frederick Douglass, an American Slave

by Frederick Douglass

I lived in Master Hugh's family about seven years. During this time, I succeeded in learning to read and write. In accomplishing this, I was compelled to resort to various stratagems. I had no regular teacher. My mistress, who had kindly commenced to instruct me, had, in compliance with the advice and direction of her husband, not only ceased to instruct, but had set her face against my being instructed by any one else. It is due, however, to my mistress to say of her, that she did not adopt this course of treatment immediately. She at first lacked the depravity indispensable to shutting me up in mental darkness. It was at least necessary for her to have some training in the exercise of irresponsible power, to make her equal to the task of treating me as though I were a brute.

My mistress was, as I have said, a kind and tenderhearted woman; and in the simplicity of her soul she commenced, when I first went to live with her, to treat me as she supposed one human being ought to treat another. In entering upon the duties of a slaveholder, she did not seem to perceive that I sustained to her the relation of a mere chattel, and that for her to treat me as a human being was not only wrong, but dangerously so. Slavery proved as injurious to her as it did to me. When I went there, she was a pious, warm, and tenderhearted woman. There was no sorrow or suffering for which she had not a tear. She had bread for the hungry, clothes for the naked, and comfort for every

153

mourner that came within her reach. Slavery soon proved its ability to divest her of these heavenly qualities. Under its influence, the tender heart became stone, and the lamblike disposition gave way to one of tigerlike fierceness. The first step in her downward course was in her ceasing to instruct me. She now commenced to practise her husband's precepts. She finally became even more violent in her opposition than her husband himself. She was not satisfied with simply doing as well as he had commanded; she seemed anxious to do better. Nothing seemed to make her more angry than to see me with a newspaper. She seemed to think that here lay the danger. I have had her rush at me with a face made all up of fury, and snatch from me a newspaper, in a manner that fully revealed her apprehension. She was an apt woman; and a little experience soon demonstrated, to her satisfaction, that education and slavery were incompatible with each other.

From this time I was most narrowly watched. If I was in a separate room any considerable length of time, I was sure to be suspected of having a book, and was at once called to give an account of myself. All this, however, was too late. The first step had been taken. Mistress, in teaching me the alphabet, had given me the *inch,* and no precaution could prevent me from taking the *ell.*

The plan which I adopted, and the one by which I was most successful, was that of making friends of all the little white boys whom I met in the street. As many of these as I could, I converted into teachers. With their kindly aid, obtained at different times and in different places, I finally succeeded in learning to read. When I was sent on errands, I always took my book with me, and by going one part of my errand quickly, I found time to get a lesson before my return. I used also to carry bread with me, enough of which was always in the house, and to which I was always welcome; for I was much better off in this regard than many of the poor white children in our neighborhood. This bread I used to bestow upon the hungry little urchins, who, in return, would give me that more valuable bread of knowledge. I am strongly tempted to give the names of two or three of those little boys, as a testimonial of the gratitude and affection I bear them; but prudence forbids;—not that it would injure me, but it might embarrass them; for it is almost an unpardonable offence to teach slaves to read in this Christian country. It is enough to say of the dear little fellows, that they lived on Philpot Street, very near Durgin and Bailey's shipyard. I used to talk this matter of slavery over with them. I would sometimes say to them, I wished I could be as free as they would be when they got to be men. "You will be free as soon as you are twenty-one, *but I am a slave for life!* Have not I as good a right to be free as you have?" These words used to trouble them; they would express for me the liveliest sympathy, and console me with the hope that something would occur by which I might be free.

Line 9. *depravity:* wickedness
Line 18. *sustained:* bore
Line 19. *chattel:* piece of property
Line 22. *pious:* religious
Line 30. *precepts:* teachings
Line 38. *apt:* quick to learn
Line 62. *testimonial:* tribute
Line 63. *prudence:* good judgment

Understanding What You Have Read

In the blank space, write the *letter* of the choice that best completes the statement.

1. The narrator was mainly concerned with _____.

   A. learning to read
   B. not causing trouble for his little white teachers
   C. gaining his freedom
   D. hiding from his master and mistress the fact that he was continuing his education

2. The passage shows that _____.

   A. no whites had less to eat than slaves
   B. slavery hurt only the slaves
   C. children can be more prejudiced than adults
   D. slavery was evil for the slave and the slaveholder

3. The reader of the passage may conclude that _____.

   A. the narrator had no kind words for his mistress because she had mistreated him
   B. slaves and poor white children were not sent to school
   C. education made a slave a better slave
   D. a basically fine human being can, under certain conditions, change for the worse

4. The mistress _____.

   A. had no skill as a teacher
   B. had no previous experience as a slaveholder
   C. never treated the narrator as a human being
   D. disregarded her husband's commands

5. The last three words in the third paragraph, "taking the *ell*," probably refer to _____.

   A. the letter "L"
   B. becoming a reader
   C. stealing
   D. learning the alphabet

Learning New Words

Line	Word	Meaning	Typical Use
15	**commence** *(v.)* kə-ˈmen(t)s	begin; start; enter upon	The troops were instructed to *commence* firing and not to stop until further orders.
		(ant. **cease, stop, end***)*	After two minutes the officer ordered all firing to *cease*.
73	**console** *(v.)* kən-ˈsōl	comfort in times of grief; lessen the suffering of; solace	I sent Myra a "get-well" card to *console* her.
50	**convert** *(v.)* kən-ˈvərt	change; alter in form; transform	The afternoon sun should *convert* the morning snow into slush.
26	**divest** *(v.)* dī-ˈvest	strip (of clothing, ornament, equipment, etc.); force to give up; deprive	The general *divested* the sergeant of his authority when he demoted him to the rank of private.
62	**gratitude** *(n.)* ˈgrat-ə-ˌt(y)üd	state of being *grateful* (thankful) because of a favor received; thankfulness	It is proper to express *gratitude* when someone does you a favor.
		(ant. **ingratitude, ungratefulness***)*	Despite all the favors I have done for Brad, he refused to let me use his glove. Did you ever hear of such *ingratitude*?
39	**incompatible** *(adj.)* ˌin-kəm-ˈpat-ə-bəl	incapable of living or acting together; not in harmony; antagonistic	If Erica and Audrey are on the committee, it will never reach an agreement; they are *incompatible*.
		(ant. **compatible***)*	I am fortunate to have such a *compatible* partner as Jeff; he is easy to get along with.
9	**indispensable** *(adj.)* ˌin-dis-ˈpen(t)-sə-bəl	absolutely necessary; essential	Food is *indispensable;* we cannot live without it.
		(ant. **dispensable***)*	When going on a hike, you can leave your hair tonic behind; it's *dispensable*.
21	**injurious** *(adj.)* in-ˈjür-ē-əs	causing *injury* (harm); harmful	Smoking is *injurious* to health.

		(*ant.* **beneficial**)	Our gym class met outdoors to enjoy the *beneficial* effects of fresh air and sunshine.
18	**perceive** (*v.*) pər-'sēv	become aware of through the senses; observe; see; realize	I *perceived* by the expression on her face that Amy was upset.
3	**stratagem** (*n.*) 'strat-ə-jəm	clever scheme for gaining an end; trick; ruse	A bandaged hand is sometimes a *stratagem* for evading a test.

Applying What You Have Learned

I. Which of the two choices makes the sentence correct? Write the *letter* of the correct answer in the space provided.

1. For Jane and her cousin to ____ is impossible; they are incompatible.

A. agree   B. quarrel

2. Instead of using a stratagem, I ____.

A. tried to disguise my voice   B. laid all my cards on the table

3. One way to show gratitude is to ____.

A. write a "thank-you" note   B. accept favors from nobody

4. Fred was ____ by your injurious remark.

A. delighted   B. hurt

5. The father consoled his daughter when he noticed her ____.

A. in tears   B. playing with matches

6. There are now ____ in the converted schoolhouse.

A. 320 students enrolled   B. four families living

7. Do you perceive what I am driving at, or ____?

A. are you afraid to take a chance   B. shall I explain it once more

8. Audrey is indispensable to our team; we will ____ without her.

A. lose   B. do just as well

9. The thief was divested ____.

A. of his loot   B. for robbery

10. Many a tale commences: "____."

A. And they lived happily ever after   B. Once upon a time

II. The meaning of each expression below can be found in the vocabulary list at the bottom of the exercise. Find that meaning and write it in the space provided.

_____ 1. lessen the suffering of

_____ 2. absolutely necessary

_____ 3. clever scheme for gaining an end

_____ 4. enter upon

_____ 5. not in harmony

_____ 6. force to give up

_____ 7. causing harm

_____ 8. become aware of

_____ 9. alter in form

_____ 10. state of being thankful for a favor received

Vocabulary List

convert	gratitude	perceive	commence	indispensable
incompatible	console	injurious	stratagem	divest

III. Synonyms and Antonyms

Fill the blanks in column A with the required synonyms and antonyms, selecting them from column B.

Column A   *Column B*

_____ 1. synonym for *deprive*   stratagem

_____ 2. antonym for *ungratefulness*   compatible

_____ 3. synonym for *realize*   convert

_____ 4. antonym for *beneficial*   divest

_____ 5. synonym for *transform*   dispensable

_____ 6. antonym for *cease*   gratitude

_____ 7. synonym for *solace*   perceive

_____ 8. antonym for *essential*   commence

_____ 9. synonym for *trick*   injurious

_____ 10. antonym for *antagonistic*   console

IV. Picture Quiz

In the blank space, write the *letter* of the picture that best fits the meaning of the sentence.

1. Which of the following three items is the most indispensable in our daily lives? ____

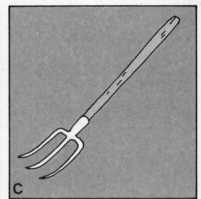

2. ____ most needs to be consoled.

3. ____ is expressing gratitude.

Learning Some Derivatives

Each word in bold type below is a *root*. The words below it are its *derivatives*.

commence *(v.)*   Were you present when the program *commenced*?

commencement *(n.)*   Were you present at the *commencement* of the program?

console *(v.)*   We tried to *console* the lost child.

consolable *(adj.)*   At first he appeared not to be *consolable*.

consolation *(n.)*   But our kindness and the candy we offered were a *consolation* to him.

convert *(v.)*   Long ago the alchemists tried to *convert* ordinary metals into gold.

convertible *(adj.)*   They believed that ordinary metals were *convertible* into gold.

conversion *(n.)*   They did not know that such *conversion* was impossible.

grateful *(adj.)*   Ralph is *grateful* for the help you gave him in Spanish.

gratefully *(adv.)*   He *gratefully* admits that without your help he would have failed.

gratitude *(n.)*   By the help you have given him, you have earned his *gratitude*.

incompatible *(adj.)*   I had to share a locker with Sam, but we quarreled from the first day; we were *incompatible*.

incompatibly *(adv.)*   The teacher perceived that we were getting along *incompatibly*.

incompatibility *(n.)*   Because of our *incompatibility*, she assigned each of us to a different partner.

indispensable *(adj.)*   A safe water supply is *indispensable*.

indispensably *(adv.)*   Man *indispensably* requires a safe water supply.

indispensability *(n.)*   No one can deny the *indispensability* of a safe water supply.

injure *(v.)*   A police record can *injure* a person's career.

injurious *(adj.)*   A police record may prove *injurious* to a person's career.

injury *(n.)*   The name of a youthful offender is usually withheld to prevent *injury* to his career.

perceive *(v.)*   Can you *perceive* a difference between the twins?

perceptible *(adj.)*   The difference is hardly *perceptible*.

perceptibly *(adv.)*	One twin is not too *perceptibly* different from the other.
perception *(n.)*	The difference between them is so slight that it escapes *perception*.
stratagem *(n.)*	When a direct attack on Troy failed, the Greeks used a *stratagem* to capture the city.
strategy *(n.)*	Their *strategy* was to offer the unsuspecting Trojans a huge wooden horse secretly filled with armed Greeks.
strategic *(adj.)*	By this *strategic* move, the Greeks were able to defeat the Trojans.
strategically *(adv.)*	The horse was *strategically* designed to get a body of armed Greeks past the walls of Troy.

Fill each blank below with the word listed previously that best fits the meaning of the sentence.

1. Some people never get over their grief; others are _____.

2. Night was almost done, and the first light of the day was gradually becoming

    _____.

3. Though we lost, it was nevertheless a(an) _____ to me to know

    that I had hit a home run.

4. An unkind word may _____ a person as severely as a hammer blow.

5. At night a(an) _____ sofa can be transformed to a bed.

6. From the _____ of the trial to its end, not a single seat in the

    courtroom was vacant.

7. I am _____ to you for keeping me informed about what was hap-

    pening in class when I was ill.

8. How can you study for your French final while watching football on TV? These are

    two _____ activities.

9. Ambush is a(an) _____ device by which a small band can surprise a

    more powerful foe.

10. The employer did not dismiss any of his most highly skilled workers because of

    their _____ to his business.

Improving Your Spelling:
Adding the Prefixes *IN-*, *IL-*, *IM-*, and *IR-*

The N in the negative prefix IN, meaning "not," as in *indecent,* often changes to another letter. For example:

1. Before a word beginning with L, the prefix IN becomes IL, as in *illegal.*

2. Before a word beginning with M or P, the prefix IN becomes IM, as in *immortal* and *improper.*

3. Before a word beginning with R, the prefix IN becomes IR, as in *irregular.*

On the other hand, the N in the negative prefix UN does not change:

$$un + able = unable$$
$$un + liked = unliked$$
$$un + married = unmarried$$
$$un + natural = unnatural$$
$$un + paid = unpaid$$
$$un + reliable = unreliable$$

PREFIXES MEANING "NOT"

Be sure to keep the double letters that sometimes form when a prefix is added to a word.

I L	+	L E G A L	=	I L L E G A L
I M	+	M O R T A L	=	I M M O R T A L
I R	+	R E G U L A R	=	I R R E G U L A R
U N	+	N A T U R A L	=	U N N A T U R A L

A. Make the following words negative by adding the prefix UN:

1. opened   _____

2. necessary   _____

3. manageable   _____

4. important   _____

5. spoiled _____

6. pleasant _____

7. touched _____

8. noticeable _____

9. likely _____

10. educated _____

B. Make the word in column II negative by adding IN, IL, IM, or IR in column I. Then write the new word in column III. (The first five lines have been done for you as examples.)

I PREFIX		II WORD		III NEW WORD
1. *in*	+	complete	=	**incomplete**
2. *il*	+	legal	=	**illegal**
3. *im*	+	mortal	=	**immortal**
4. *im*	+	proper	=	**improper**
5. *ir*	+	regular	=	**irregular**
6. _____	+	possible	=	_____
7. _____	+	effective	=	_____
8. _____	+	logical	=	_____
9. _____	+	responsible	=	_____
10. _____	+	mature	=	_____
11. _____	+	convenient	=	_____
12. _____	+	religious	=	_____
13. _____	+	modest	=	_____
14. _____	+	moral	=	_____
15. _____	+	legible	=	_____
16. _____	+	resistible	=	_____
17. _____	+	patient	=	_____
18. _____	+	sane	=	_____
19. _____	+	perceptible	=	_____

20. _____ + replaceable = _____

21. _____ + material = _____

22. _____ + literate = _____

23. _____ + probable = _____

24. _____ + reducible = _____

25. _____ + compatible = _____

26. _____ + reversible = _____

27. _____ + legitimate = _____

28. _____ + movable = _____

29. _____ + pure = _____

30. _____ + consistent = _____

Correct Usage: *Who, Whom,* and *Whose*

1. **WHO** is used as a subject.

"My mistress, *who* had kindly commenced to instruct me . . ."

(*who* is the subject of the verb *had commenced*)

Who is absent?

(*who* is the subject of the verb *is*)

2. **WHOM** is used:

(a) as an object of a verb.

Frederick Douglass made friends of the boys *whom* he met in the street.

(*whom* is the object of the verb *met*)

Whom did you see?

(*whom* is the object of the verb *did see*)

(b) as an object of a preposition.

Dan is the student with *whom* I changed places.

(*whom* is the object of the preposition *with*)

From *whom* did you get the information?

(*whom* is the object of the preposition *from*)

3. **WHOSE** indicates ownership.

The girl *whose* watch you found is my cousin.

(*whose* indicates ownership of *watch*)

Whose glove is this?

(*whose* indicates ownership of *glove*)

CAUTION: Do not confuse *whose* with the contraction *who's* meaning "who is."

Who's (Who is) absent?

Complete the sentence by inserting *who, whom, whose,* or *who's.*

1. Frederick Douglass gave bread to the hungry lads, _____, in return, gave him the more valuable bread of knowledge.

2. To _____ should we send the check?

3. I could not tell _____ answer was correct.

4. _____ should we ask?

5. _____ on the telephone?

6. This is my sister Sue, _____ is in the ninth grade.

7. _____ turn is it?

8. Do you know by _____ the book was written?

9. At the entrance I met a teacher _____ I had a year ago.

10. _____ was elected?

11. The girl _____ father is driving us to the game says we should be ready at 7:15.

12. There were only three students _____ received marks higher than 90.

13. _____ making his report today?

14. With _____ are you going to the movie?

15. On the bus I met someone _____ you know quite well.

16. Paul is visiting a classmate _____ plays the guitar.

17. Everyone knew for _____ the warning was meant.

18. _____ is she inviting to her party?

19. Those _____ came late had to stand all through the performance.

20. The teacher from _____ I got the highest mark is Mrs. Seiden.

REVIEW OF GROUP III

I. Fill in the missing letters of the word at the right of the definition. Then write the complete word in the blank space.

DEFINITION	WORD	COMPLETE WORD
1. violent and uncontrollable anger	_ _ GE	_____
2. second of two	_ _ _ _ ER	_____
3. sudden inclination to act	IMP _ _ _ _ _	_____
4. absolutely necessary	_ _ _ _ SPENSABLE	_____
5. as a rule	GENER _ _ _ _	_____
6. choice between two things	_ _ _ _ RNATIVE	_____
7. make a forceful forward movement	LUN _ _	_____
8. fight against	_ _ SIST	_____
9. not in harmony	INCOM _ _ _ IBLE	_____
10. move about slowly and stealthily	_ _ OWL	_____
11. comfort in time of grief	CONS _ _ _	_____
12. long, sharp, pointed tooth	_ _ NG	_____
13. get away from, by skill or cleverness	EV _ _ _	_____
14. thick growth of bushes and shrubs	_ _ USH	_____
15. soft tissue in most bone cavities	MAR _ _ _	_____
16. clever scheme for gaining an end	STRA _ _ _ EM	_____

17. wildly or uncontrollably

excited   _ _ _ _ ZIED   _____

18. act of happening again   RE _ _ RRENCE   _____

19. draw away to a different

subject   _ _ _ TRACT   _____

20. twist and turn this way

and that   _ _ ITHE   _____

II. For each italicized word in column A, write the best _antonym_ from column B.

Column A	_Column B_
_____ **1.** feeling of _ungratefulness_	insolent
_____ **2.** _courteous_ reply	exclude
_____ **3.** _beneficial_ effects	ignore
_____ **4.** _heed_ traffic signs	commence
_____ **5.** with _confidence_	yield
_____ **6.** likely to _resist_	zeal
_____ **7.** _end_ on time	gratitude
_____ **8.** absence of _apathy_	submission
_____ **9.** _admit_ no one	apprehension
_____ **10.** total _resistance_	injurious

III. To each line below, add a word that has the _same meaning_ as the first two words on the line. Choose your words from the Vocabulary List at the bottom of the exercise.

1. transform, change, _____

2. beginner, apprentice, _____

3. restrain, curb, _____

4. earlier, prior, _____

5. whine, cry, _____

6. outrage, insult, _____

7. deprive, strip, _____

8. tip, incline, _____

9. obviously, evidently, _____

10. realize, see, _____

Vocabulary List

former	cub
convert	tilt
indignity	whimper
perceive	apparently
check	divest

IV. **A.** Fill in the missing letter of the incomplete word in column A. Then write the complete word in column B.

Column A　　　　　*Column B*

1. occurr __ nce　　_____

2. min __ te　　_____

3. confid __ nt　　_____

4. i __ convenient　　_____

5. resist __ nce　　_____

6. gramm __ r　　_____

7. assist __ nt　　_____

8. i __ logical　　_____

9. appli __ nce　　_____

10. sep __ rate　　_____

11. vehem __ nt　　_____

12. w __ men　　_____

13. ignor __ nt　　_____

14. i __ patient　　_____

15. allegi __ nce　　_____

16. sug __ r　　_____

17. interfer __ nce　　_____

18. i __ responsible　　_____

19. observ __ nt _____

20. i __ moral _____

B. Write the new word.

WORD + SUFFIX = NEW WORD

1. compel + ed   = _____

2. offer + ing   = _____

3. repeal + ed   = _____

4. commit + ment = _____

5. label + ed   = _____

6. refer + ing   = _____

7. benefit + ing = _____

8. regret + able = _____

9. permit + ing = _____

10. prefer + ence = _____

V. Complete each sentence below with the most appropriate word from the following vocabulary list.

Vocabulary List

former	incompatible	lunge
gratitude	latter	frantic
indignity	alternative	indispensable
convert	writhe	check

1. Near dismissal time some students are so impatient that they _____ in their seats.

2. I hope Laura and I will not be assigned to the same committee because we are

_____ .

3. The opposing team tried to _____ our advance at the twenty-yard line, but we swept on to a touchdown.

4. To bite the hand that feeds you is no way to show _____ .

5. If you decide neither to resist nor to surrender, you will still have a third

_____ : to try to arrange a truce.

6. Both silver and gold are precious metals, but the _____ is more costly.

7. When you cross the border, you will have to _____ some of your money to Canadian currency.

8. The _____ screams of a lost child distracted our attention.

9. If Joan quits, we can still put on the play; she's not _____.

10. To be called lazy is an insult, but to be labeled as a liar is a far greater _____.

VI. On lines B and C, write the required forms of the italicized word on line A.

1. A. Are you *resistant* to change?

   B. Do you _____ change because you prefer things to remain as they are?

   C. Do you go along with new ideas, or do you offer _____?

2. A. I have an *impulse* to swing at the first pitch.

   B. I _____ swing at the first pitch.

   C. I am _____ about swinging at the first pitch.

3. A. Some members of the squad refuse to *submit* to your authority.

   B. They will not _____ obey your orders.

   C. They will not be _____.

4. A. Certain plant diseases, if *unchecked*, can destroy entire crops.

   B. Farmers spray crops to _____ plant disease.

   C. They have successfully used sprays as a _____ to crop destruction.

5. A. Before the interview, I was *apprehensive*.

   B. I came to the interview with _____.

   C. I entered the interviewer's office _____.

6. A. Arthur and Alex cannot work as a team because they are *incompatible*.

   B. They are _____ matched and should be separated.

   C. Because of their _____, they are unlikely to produce any useful work.

7. A. Why were you *insolent* to your cousin?

B. Why did you _____ slam the door in his face?

C. There is no reason for such _____.

8. A. The *prowler* sighted near the farm could have been a fox or a wolf.

B. At night these beasts _____ in search of food.

C. A fox might have been on the _____ on the outskirts of the farm.

9. A. The picnic is *exclusively* for members who have paid their dues.

B. We plan to _____ all others.

C. The threat of _____ from the picnic has already made several members pay up.

10. A. Harvey's cough is apt to *recur* when he is run down.

B. He has a _____ cough.

C. It seems to get worse with each _____.

11. A. It is possible to *convert* some waste material into useful products.

B. Some waste materials are _____ to useful products.

C. One example is the _____ of dead leaves into compost for fertilizing the soil.

12. A. False rumors may *injure* a person's reputation.

B. False rumors may do serious _____ to a person's reputation.

C. False rumors may be _____.

13. A. My opponent *evaded* me.

B. My opponent was _____.

C. My opponent _____ stepped to one side.

14. A. You ought to call on Marie to *console* her.

B. She does not seem _____, but I know you can cheer her up.

C. I am sure she will find _____ in your words of sympathy.

15. A. We are *grateful* for your help.

B. We _____ appreciate what you have done for us.

C. We wish to express our _____.

16. A. The commander's *strategy* was to retreat to a more favorable position.

B. He ordered a retreat for _____ reasons.

C. He perceived that, under the circumstances, retreat was _____ necessary.

17. A. No one has shown greater *zeal* in selling tickets than Barbara.

B. No one has been more _____ than she.

C. Barbara is working _____ to sell more tickets.

18. A. The fog made it difficult to *perceive* what lay ahead.

B. Nearby objects were barely _____.

C. The fog made _____ difficult.

19. A. It would be very difficult for a library to be without dictionaries and encyclopedias; such reference books are *indispensable*.

B. Reference books are _____ needed.

C. Because of their _____, reference books are among the first that a library should purchase.

20. A. On long trips, Dad and Mom *alternate* behind the wheel.

B. Before starting out, Dad usually gives Mom the _____ of driving.

C. They change places every hour so that each of them is _____ the driver or a passenger.

READING SELECTION 13

Sherlock Holmes, the famous detective, has been listening to Mr. Jabez Wilson, who has come for help. In walks Dr. Watson, Holmes's close friend and assistant. Holmes proceeds to inform Watson about the Wilson case.

from

The Redheaded League

by Sir Arthur Conan Doyle

"Now, Mr. Jabez Wilson here has been good enough to call upon me this morning, and to begin a narrative which promises to be one of the most singular which I have listened to for some time. You have heard me remark that the strangest and most unique things are very often connected not with the larger but ⁵ with the smaller crimes, and occasionally, indeed, where there is room for doubt whether any positive crime has been committed. As far as I have heard, it is impossible for me to say whether the present case is an instance of crime or not, but the course of events is certainly among the most singular that I have ever ¹⁰ listened to. Perhaps, Mr. Wilson, you would have the great kindness to recommence your narrative. I ask you not merely because my friend Dr. Watson has not heard the opening part but also because the peculiar nature of the story makes me anxious to have every possible detail from your lips. As a rule, when I have ¹⁵ heard some slight indication of the course of events, I am able to guide myself by the thousands of other similar cases which occur to my memory. In the present instance I am forced to admit that the facts are, to the best of my belief, unique."

The portly client puffed out his chest with an appearance of ²⁰ some little pride and pulled a dirty and wrinkled newspaper from the inside pocket of his great-coat. As he glanced down the ad-

vertisement column, with his head thrust forward and the paper
flattened out upon his knee, I took a good look at the man and
25 endeavored, after the fashion of my companion, to read the indi-
cations which might be presented by his dress or appearance.

I did not gain very much, however, by my inspection. Our
visitor bore every mark of being an average commonplace British
tradesman, obese, pompous, and slow. He wore rather baggy gray
30 shepherd's check trousers, a not overclean black frock coat, unbuttoned in the front, and a drab waistcoat with a heavy brassy
Albert chain, and a square pierced bit of metal dangling down
as an ornament. A frayed top hat and a faded brown overcoat
with a wrinkled velvet collar lay upon a chair beside him. Al-
35 together, look as I would, there was nothing remarkable about the
man save his blazing red head, and the expression of extreme
chagrin and discontent upon his features.

Sherlock Holmes's quick eye took in my occupation, and he
shook his head with a smile as he noticed my questioning glances.
40 "Beyond the obvious facts that he has at some time done manual
labor, that he takes snuff, that he is a Freemason, that he has
been in China, and that he has done a considerable amount of
writing lately, I can deduce nothing else."

Mr. Jabez Wilson started up in his chair, with his forefinger
45 upon the paper, but his eyes upon my companion.

"How, in the name of good fortune, did you know all that,
Mr. Holmes?" he asked. "How did you know, for example, that I
did manual labor? It's as true as gospel, for I began as a ship's
carpenter."

50 "Your hands, my dear sir. Your right hand is quite a size
larger than your left. You have worked with it, and the muscles
are more developed."

Line 37. *chagrin:* disappointment
Line 41. *Freemason:* member of a worldwide, secret society

Understanding What You Have Read

In the blank space, write the *letter* of the choice that best completes the statement.

1. In the opening paragraph, Holmes _____.

  A. addresses first Dr. Watson and then Mr. Wilson
  B. addresses Dr. Watson but not Mr. Wilson
  C. is forced to admit that he cannot help Mr. Wilson
  D. addresses first Mr. Wilson and then Dr. Watson

2. In the second paragraph, "I" refers to _____.

  A. Holmes, and "companion" to Mr. Wilson
  B. Holmes, and "companion" to Dr. Watson

C. Dr. Watson, and "companion" to Holmes
D. Dr. Watson, and "companion" to Mr. Wilson

3. The passage suggests that _____ .

A. Mr. Wilson is a well-to-do merchant
B. a newspaper advertisement has something to do with the case
C. Dr. Watson is not interested in the case
D. some of Holmes's statements about Mr. Wilson's past may not be true

4. The fact that Mr. Wilson is _____ escapes Dr. Watson's attention.

A. right-handed
B. redheaded
C. slow
D. not neatly dressed

5. The passage indicates that _____ .

A. Holmes has not the slightest doubt about his ability to solve the case
B. Wilson has finished telling his story
C. Holmes is certain that a crime has been committed
D. Dr. Watson has not said anything to Holmes or to the visitor

Learning New Words

Line	Word	Meaning	Typical Use
20	**client** (n.) 'klī-ənt	person who engages the professional services of another; customer; patron	If you need insurance get in touch with Watts and Miller. Dad has been one of their *clients* for years.
28	**commonplace** (adj.) 'käm-ən-ˌplās (ant. **extraordinary**)	ordinary; unremarkable; neither new nor interesting	The plot is *commonplace*, like that of most Westerns, but the acting is *extraordinary*.
43	**deduce** (v.) di-'d(y)üs	reason out or conclude from known facts; infer	From the fact that Dr. Compton's car was on your driveway, I *deduced* that someone in your family was ill.
33	**frayed** (adj.) 'frād	worn; ragged; worn out	I have given that sweater a great deal of wear; it is getting *frayed* at the cuffs.
40	**manual** (adj.) 'man-yə(-wə)l	1. involving the hands	A good typist has a high degree of *manual* skill.

		2. hand-operated	In cars with *manual* transmission, the driver shifts gears by hand.
		3. requiring or using physical skill or energy	Because he likes working with his hands, Frank will go into carpentry or some other kind of *manual* occupation.
12	**narrative** *(n.)* 'nar-ət-iv	something that is *narrated* (told); story; tale; account	After dinner, we listened to my cousin's *narrative* of his camping trip.
33	**ornament** *(n.)* 'or-nə-mənt	Something that adorns or adds beauty; decoration; embellishment	With a plain dress, Grandma wears a jeweled pin, a necklace, or some other simple *ornament*.
29	**pompous** *(adj.)* 'päm-pəs	making an appearance of importance or dignity; self-important	Sheila did not wear her medal because she felt it would make her seem *pompous*.
		(ant. **lowly***)*	Andrew Carnegie rose from the *lowly* position of bobbin-boy to become a superintendent of a railroad.
20	**portly** *(adj.)* 'port-lē	heavy of body; stout; corpulent; obese	Regent Tailors can outfit men and boys of all sizes, whether short or tall, lean or *portly*.
		(ant. **lean, skinny***)*	
19	**unique** *(adj.)* yu̇-'nēk	being the only one of its kind in existence; having no like or equal; unparalleled; singular	Do you realize that everyone is a *unique* individual, since no two persons are exactly alike?
		(ant. **common, ordinary***)*	Don't think your mistake is unique. Others have made it, too. In fact, it is quite *common*.

Applying What You Have Learned

I. Which of the two choices makes the sentence correct? Write the *letter* of the correct answer in the space provided.

1. Her drawings are commonplace; there is nothing ____ about them.

    A. remarkable   B. ordinary

2. One of the teams has the pompous name of ____.

A. "Grand Monarchs"   B. "Blue Jays"

3. To ____ is a unique achievement.

A. be reelected President   B. break the world's record in the high
   of the United States   jump

4. You cannot deduce anything unless you start with ____.

A. facts   B. opinions

5. The ____ and his client were here a moment ago.

A. lawyer   B. customer

6. She wore a ____ as an ornament.

A. puzzled look   B. bracelet

7. ____ requires manual skill

A. Listening to an opera   B. Rowing a boat

8. Uncle Jim has become portly; he has ____ much weight.

A. lost   B. gained

9. It was a narrative that I had not ____ before.

A. heard   B. eaten

10. Some trousers become frayed; others ____.

A. are hard to clean   B. wear like iron

II. The meaning of each expression below can be found in the vocabulary list at the bottom of the exercise. Find that meaning and write it in the space provided.

_____ **1.** involving the hands

_____ **2.** neither new nor interesting

_____ **3.** having no like or equal

_____ **4.** something that is told

_____ **5.** something that adorns

_____ **6.** reason out from known facts

_____ **7.** heavy of body

_____ 8. person who engages the professional services of another

_____ 9. worn out

_____ 10. making an appearance of importance

Vocabulary List

ornament	client
frayed	commonplace
narrative	unique
manual	deduce
pompous	portly

III. Synonyms and Antonyms

A. Replace the italicized word or expression with a *synonym* from the vocabulary list at the bottom of the exercise.

_____ 1. The Puritans wore very plain clothing, without *decoration* or embellishment.

_____ 2. English bicycles are equipped with *hand* brakes.

_____ 3. The accountant was about to leave his office when a *customer* called.

_____ 4. Have you read "An Occurrence at Owl Creek Bridge"? It is a most unusual *tale.*

_____ 5. Dad will not wear a shirt with a *ragged* collar.

_____ 6. What have you been able to *infer* from the facts I have given you?

B. Replace each italicized word with an *antonym* from the vocabulary list.

_____ 7. The table seemed to be a *common* piece of furniture.

_____ 8. The person we talked to impressed us as being a *lowly* individual.

_____ 9. The room was decorated with *extraordinary* furnishings.

_____ 10. At the next station, a *lean*, middle-aged lady got off the train.

Vocabulary List

deduce	commonplace
narrative	manual
portly	pompous
frayed	ornament
unique	client

IV. Picture Quiz

In the space below, write the *letter* of the picture that best fits the meaning of the sentence.

1. ____ is not using manual skills.

2. ____ is a useful wall ornament.

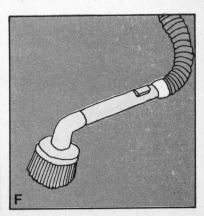

179

3. ____ is frayed.

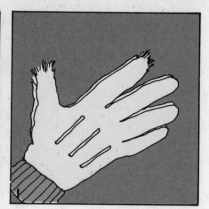

Learning Some Derivatives

Each word in bold type below is a *root*. The words below it are its *derivatives*.

deduce *(v.)*	From the few clues we have so far, we can *deduce* very little.
deducible *(adj.)*	This much is *deducible:* the thief, whoever he is, was careful not to leave many clues behind.
deduction *(n.)*	About the only *deduction* we can make at this time is that the thief is a shrewd operator.
manual *(adj.)*	In the olden days, pumping water from a well was a *manual* operation.
manually *(adv.)*	Today, water does not have to be pumped *manually*—we have electric pumps.
narrate *(v.)*	Have you heard my cousin Joel *narrate* the details of his trip to Alaska?
narrative *(n.)*	It's an exciting *narrative*.
narrator *(n.)*	Joel is an excellent *narrator*.
narration *(n.)*	He excels in *narration*.
ornament *(n.)*	Buttons and bows can be useful as *ornaments*.
ornament *(v.)*	Buttons, for example, of various colors, shapes, and sizes, are used to *ornament* garments.
ornamental *(adj.)*	Bows are prized for their *ornamental* value in gift-wrapping.
ornamentation *(n.)*	Buttons and bows are widely used in *ornamentation*.
pomp *(n.)*	The old emperor enjoyed the *pomp* and splendor of reviewing his troops as their commander-in-chief.

pompous (adj.)	A pompous man, he loved to appear in public in dress uniform.
pompously (adv.)	His uniforms were pompously ornamented with rows of medals and ribbons.
pomposity (n.)	The emperor's son, however, disapproved of such pomposity; he disliked parades, titles, and uniforms.
portly (adj.)	One clown was tall and lean; the other was short and portly.
portliness (n.)	Because of his portliness, the short clown could not run too fast.
unique (adj.)	Gibraltar is in a unique position near the entrance to the Mediterranean Sea.
uniquely (adv.)	Gibraltar is uniquely situated.
uniqueness (n.)	Gibraltar has been highly prized as a naval base because of the uniqueness of its location.

Fill each blank below with the word in the list above that best fits the meaning of the sentence.

1. Gordon often spoils a story in telling it; he is not a good _____.

2. The new office manager _____ insisted that all of the clerks address him as "Sir."

3. When I saw your books were still on your desk, I made the _____ that you had not yet left for home.

4. The _____ of St. Augustine, Florida, is that it is the oldest city in the United States, having been founded in 1565.

5. From his _____, you might deduce that he likes to eat.

6. As a little child, I loved to hear Grandma _____ fairy tales.

7. This has been a(an) _____ wet year; we have had more rain than in any previous year on record.

8. Before the invention of the electric can opener, all can openers were operated _____.

9. When Joe is not playing his handsome guitar, he uses it to _____ the wall of his room.

10. Unfortunately the owner's name was not _____ from the contents of the purse.

It is often possible to change derivatives into root words by dropping prefixes and suffixes.

DISCONTENT – DIS   = CONTENT
DEVELOPED – ED   = DEVELOP
UNBUTTONED – UN, ED = BUTTON

CAUTIONS

1. If an E was dropped when the suffix was added, put back the E.

BLAZE   + ING = BLAZING
BLAZING – ING = BLAZE

GLANCE   + ED = GLANCED
GLANCED – ED = GLANCE

2. If a final consonant was doubled when the suffix was added, undouble it.

COMMIT   + ED = COMMITTED
COMMITTED – ED = COMMIT

BAG   + Y = BAGGY
BAGGY – Y = BAG

3. If a final Y was changed to I when the suffix was added, change it back to Y.

HURRY   + ED = HURRIED
HURRIED – ED = HURRY

HAPPY   + NESS = HAPPINESS
HAPPINESS – NESS = HAPPY

Write the root word in the column at the right.

1. remarkable — able = _____

2. dangling — ing = _____

3. bigger — er = _____

4. disappearance — dis *and* ance = _____

5. foggy — y = _____

6. unopened — un *and* ed = _____

7. pompous — ous = _____

8. planning — ing = _____

9. unhappiness — un *and* ness = _____

10. permitted — ed = _____

11. advertisement — ment = _____

12. brassy — y = _____

13. unreliable — un *and* able = _____

14. improperly — im *and* ly = _____

15. listener — er = _____

16. flattened — en *and* ed = _____

17. frayed — ed = _____

18. hottest — est = _____

19. indescribable — in *and* able = _____

20. recommence — re = _____

21. visitor — or = _____

22. inescapable — in *and* able = _____

23. compelled — ed = _____

24. weariness — ness = _____

25. wrinkled — ed = _____

Grammar: Active and Passive Verbs

1. An *active verb* describes an action done by its subject.

   Sherlock Holmes <u>solved</u> the case.

                        v

   (The verb *solved* is active because it describes an action done by *Sherlock Holmes,* its subject.)

2. A *passive verb* describes an action done to its subject.

   The case <u>was solved</u> by Sherlock Holmes.

                v

   (The verb *was solved* is passive because it describes an action done to the *case,* its subject.)

   Here are some further examples of active and passive verbs:

   ACTIVE: Carelessness *causes* accidents.
   PASSIVE: Accidents *are caused* by carelessness.

   ACTIVE: She *will write* the letter.
   PASSIVE: The letter *will be written* by her.

   ACTIVE: The children *ate* the chocolates.
   PASSIVE: The chocolates *were eaten* by the children.

3. You can form the passive by adding some form of the verb *to be* (*is, was, will be, has been,* etc.) to the past participle (third principal part) of a verb. Examples:

is broken	*has been collected*	*was introduced*
will be told	*are being sent*	*were misplaced*

I. In the space provided, rewrite the sentence, changing the verb from active to passive.

   SAMPLE: The Giants won the game.

                   The game was won by the Giants.

1. A passerby noticed the fire.

_____

2. Exercise develops muscles.

_____

3. Mr. Wilson did manual labor.

_____

4. Dad will pay the bill.

_____

5. The courts enforce the laws.

_____

4. In general, use *active* verbs. They will enable you to express yourself more clearly, more briefly, and more naturally.

Compare these sentences:

PASSIVE: Our business was minded by us.   (6 words)
ACTIVE: We minded our business.   (4 words)

Not only does the second sentence use fewer words, but it is clearer and more natural. The use of the passive verb in the first sentence makes that sentence unnatural and awkward.

Active verbs are far more common in English than passive verbs. Avoid passive verbs, especially when they cause awkwardness.

5. One good use of passive verbs is to help you avoid the vague pronoun *they,* as in the following:

POOR: *They* manufacture automobiles in Detroit.

(Who is *they*? The sentence is not clear on this point. Probably *they* is a vague reference to the automobile factories, or the automobile manufacturers.)

In a case like the above, use a passive verb to avoid vagueness:

BETTER: Automobiles *are manufactured* in Detroit.

II. Improve each of the following sentences by rewriting it with an active or a passive verb, as needed.

SAMPLES: An agreement will be entered into by us.
We will enter into an agreement.

They sell refreshments in the lobby.
Refreshments are sold in the lobby.

1. Six kittens were had by our cat.

_____

2. A good look at Mr. Wilson was taken by Dr. Watson.

_____

3. Your help is urgently needed by me.

_____

4. They grow excellent corn in Iowa.

_____

5. A good time will be had by you.

_____

6. Their new uniforms were received by the players.

_____

7. Baggy pants were worn by Mr. Wilson.

_____

8. They arrest reckless drivers in this town.

_____

9. Our seats will be taken promptly by us.

_____

10. The moon was jumped over by the cow.

_____

It is fifty below zero. Down a frozen waterway, a team of dogs is dragging a sled with a coffin lashed to it. Ahead of the dogs, a man in snowshoes is plodding his way through the snow, and behind the sled is a second man. A third man has died; his corpse is in the coffin.

from

White Fang

by Jack London

An hour went by, and a second hour. The pale light of the short sunless day was beginning to fade, when a faint far cry arose on the still air. It soared upward with a swift rush, till it reached its topmost note, where it persisted, palpitant and tense, and then slowly died away. It might have been a lost soul wailing, had it not been invested with a certain sad fierceness and hungry eagerness. The front man turned his head until his eyes met the eyes of the man behind. And then, across the narrow oblong box, each nodded to the other.

A second cry arose, piercing the silence with needlelike shrillness. Both men located the sound. It was to the rear, somewhere in the snow expanse they had just traversed. A third and answering cry arose, also to the rear and to the left of the second cry.

"They're after us, Bill," said the man at the front.

His voice sounded hoarse and unreal, and he had spoken with apparent effort.

"Meat is scarce," answered his comrade. "I ain't seen a rabbit sign for days."

Thereafter they spoke no more, though their ears were keen for the hunting-cries that continued to rise behind them.

At the fall of darkness they swung the dogs into a cluster of spruce trees on the edge of the waterway and made a camp. The coffin, at the side of the fire, served for seat and table. The wolf-

dogs, clustered on the far side of the fire, snarled and bickered
among themselves, but evinced no inclination to stray off into
the darkness.

"Seems to me, Henry, they're stayin' remarkable close to
camp," Bill commented.

Henry, squatting over the fire and settling the pot of coffee
with a piece of ice, nodded. Nor did he speak till he had taken his
seat on the coffin and begun to eat.

"They know where their hides is safe," he said. "They'd sooner
eat grub than be grub. They're pretty wise, them dogs."

Bill shook his head. "Oh, I don't know."

His comrade looked at him curiously. "First time I ever heard
you say anythin' about their not bein' wise."

"Henry," said the other, munching with deliberation the beans
he was eating, "did you happen to notice the way them dogs
kicked up when I was a-feedin' 'em?"

"They did cut up more'n usual," Henry acknowledged.

"How many dogs 've we got, Henry?"

"Six."

"Well, Henry . . ." Bill stopped for a moment, in order that his
words might gain greater significance. "As I was sayin', Henry,
we've got six dogs. I took six fish out of the bag. I gave one fish
to each dog, an', Henry, I was one fish short."

"You counted wrong."

"We've got six dogs," the other reiterated dispassionately.
"I took out six fish. One Ear didn't get no fish. I come back to the
bag afterward an' got 'im his fish."

"We've only got six dogs," Henry said.

"Henry," Bill went on, "I won't say they was all dogs, but
there was seven of 'em that got fish."

Understanding What You Have Read

In the blank space, write the *letter* of the choice that best completes the statement or answers the question.

1. Bill suggests that ____ .

   A. he made a mistake in counting
   B. one of the dogs got two fish
   C. his imagination played a trick on him
   D. one of the animals that got fish was not a dog

2. Which of the following is untrue? ____

   A. The sun shone only a short time each day.
   B. The men and dogs did not travel at night.
   C. The men did not see who was making the cries.
   D. One Ear is the name of a dog.

3. The dogs _____.

    A. made answering cries
    B. did not like fish
    C. were part wolf
    D. were fed by Henry

4. The cries _____.

    A. came from a single source
    B. were made by hungry creatures
    C. could be heard on all sides of the traveling party
    D. were only three in number

5. According to the evidence in the passage, _____.

    A. the dogs feel unsafe, but not the men
    B. both the men and the dogs feel safe
    C. both the men and the dogs feel unsafe
    D. the men feel unsafe, but not the dogs

Learning New Words

Line	Word	Meaning	Typical Use
40	**acknowledge** *(v.)* ak-'näl-ij	admit to be true; admit; concede	At first Jimmy denied that he was the owner of the water pistol, but he finally *acknowledged* that it was his.
		*(ant. **deny**)*	
24	**bicker** *(v.)* 'bik-ər	quarrel over petty things; wrangle; squabble	Almost every day, I would hear the brothers quarrel, and I often wondered what they were *bickering* about.
21	**cluster** *(n.)* kləs-tər	number of similar things growing or grouped together; bunch	Mother bought a *cluster* of red grapes that weighed more than two pounds.
48	**dispassionately** *(adv.)* dis-'pash-(ə-)nət-lē	in a *dispassionate* (calm) manner; calmly; coolly	The first defendant listened *dispassionately* to the verdict; he showed no emotion at all.
		*(ant. **passionately**)*	But the second shouted *passionately:* "It's a frame-up! I am innocent!"

189

25	**evince** *(v.)* i-'vin(t)s	display clearly; show; reveal	The parents were alarmed, but in the children's presence they *evinced* no sign of fright.
2	**fade** *(v.)* 'fād	grow dim; lose brightness or color; disappear gradually; wither	It was getting late. Daylight was *fading*. Soon it would be dark.
4	**persist** *(v.)* pər-'sist	1. go on resolutely despite opposition, warnings, or pleas; persevere (*ant.* **desist**)	Why do you *persist* in calling me Deborah? Please call me Debbie. The government order directed the company to *desist* from misleading advertising.
		2. last on and on; continue to exist	The cold medicines have not helped; my cough has *persisted*.
44	**significance** *(n.)* sig-'nif-i-kən(t)s	quality of being *significant* (important); importance; consequence; meaning (*ant.* **insignificance**)	Today's brief quiz was not too important. The final will be of far greater *significance*. Dan insists on paying back the nickel he borrowed, but I told him to forget about that debt because of its *insignificance*.
3	**soar** *(v.)* 'sō(ə)r	fly upward; move upward; rise; ascend	Stock prices *soared* in the morning but fell sharply by mid-afternoon.
12	**traverse** *(v.)* trə-'vərs	pass through or over; cross	Thousands of pioneer families *traversed* the Great Plains in covered wagons.

Applying What You Have Learned

I. Which of the two choices makes the sentence correct? Write the *letter* of the correct answer in the space provided.

1. Will the pain ____ or persist?

    A. continue   B. stop

2. She talked dispassionately, as if she were ____.

    A. not the least bit concerned   B. out for revenge

3. The ____ soared.

    A. kite   B. lion

4. In his campaign speeches, Henry evinced ____.

A. his opponents

B. a sense of humor

5. Ruth ____, but she will not acknowledge it.

A. admits her mistake

B. knows she is wrong

6. We traversed the playing field ____.

A. on foot

B. without leaving our seats

7. There is no reason for them to bicker, since they ____.

A. both agree

B. do not trust each other

8. You said these details are ____, but I find them of no significance.

A. meaningless

B. important

9. As dawn approaches, the stars fade and ____.

A. disappear

B. grow bright

10. When I entered the gym, I saw a cluster of my friends, and I wondered why they were all ____.

A. avoiding one another

B. together

II. The meaning of each expression below can be found in the vocabulary list on the next page. Find that meaning and write it in the space provided.

_____ **1.** move upward

_____ **2.** display clearly

_____ **3.** number of similar things grouped together

_____ **4.** grow dim

_____ **5.** pass through or over

_____ **6.** admit to be true

_____ **7.** quality of being important

_____ **8.** quarrel over petty things

_____ **9.** in a calm manner

_____ **10.** go on resolutely despite opposition

Vocabulary List

cluster	evince
traverse	dispassionately
bicker	fade
persist	acknowledge
soar	significance

III. Synonyms and Antonyms

Fill the blanks in column A with the required synonyms or antonyms, selecting them from column B.

Column A   *Column B*

_____ 1. synonym for *bunch*   insignificance

_____ 2. antonym for *importance*   desist

_____ 3. synonym for *cross*   passionately

_____ 4. synonym for *rise*   acknowledge

_____ 5. antonym for *deny*   evince

_____ 6. antonym for *calmly*   traverse

_____ 7. synonym for *wrangle*   cluster

_____ 8. synonym for *show*   fade

_____ 9. antonym for *persevere*   soar

_____ 10. synonym for *wither*   bicker

IV. Picture Quiz

In the space below, write the *letter* of the picture that best fits the meaning of the sentence.

1. ____ seems to be viewing the election dispassionately.

192

2. There is a cluster in ____.

3. No ____ ever soars.

Learning Some Derivatives

Each word in bold type below is a *root*. The words below it are its *derivatives*.

acknowledge *(v.)*	To hoist a white flag is to *acknowledge* defeat.
acknowledgment *(n.)*	The raising of a white flag is an *acknowledgment* of surrender.
bicker *(v.)*	The difference between your price and my offer is trifling; let's not *bicker* about it.
bickering *(n.)*	All right. I'll give you another quarter, if that will stop the *bickering*.
cluster *(n.)*	By 9 A.M. a *cluster* of people had gathered on the steps of the library, waiting for the doors to open.
cluster *(v.)*	Before leaving, all of us *clustered* around Harvey to wish him once more a happy birthday.

dispassionate *(adj.)*	If my brother were involved in a fight, I could not be a *dispassionate* onlooker.
dispassionately *(adv.)*	If I were to see my brother being hurt, I could not stand by *dispassionately*.
persist *(v.)*	The convict *persisted* in his efforts to get a new trial.
persistent *(adj.)*	He was *persistent;* he wrote hundreds of letters to public officials.
persistently *(adv.)*	Several lawyers told him there was no hope, but he *persistently* continued his campaign.
persistence *(n.)*	His *persistence* was finally rewarded when a higher court ordered that he be given a retrial.
significant *(adj.)*	At the first trial, the convict's attorney had not introduced a certain piece of evidence because he felt it was not *significant*.
significantly *(adv.)*	The convict now feels that that piece of evidence would have *significantly* affected the verdict.
significance *(n.)*	A bit of evidence that was considered unimportant may turn out to be of the greatest *significance*.

Fill each blank below with the word listed previously that best fits the meaning of the sentence.

1. Despite management's plea that it does not have the money, labor has been _____ in its demand for higher wages.

2. Management is ready to _____ that the cost of living has gone up sharply.

3. At the bargaining table, the representatives of both labor and management have at times lost their tempers; only the arbitrator has managed to remain _____.

4. When the representative of management made its first wage offer, labor said it was of no _____ and refused to consider it.

5. Labor has _____ sought a minimum salary increase of 5%.

6. Management has shown equal _____ in limiting increases to no more than 3%.

194

7. Labor has said it will not return to the bargaining table until management makes a

_____ wage offer.

8. There is a rumor that the dispute over wages has been settled, but there is still some

_____ over working conditions.

9. If wages are raised _____ , there will probably be no strike.

10. Whenever a management or labor official emerges from the conference room, the

reporters _____ around him to learn of the latest developments.

Improving Your Spelling:
Learning Some More Homonyms

Homonyms, you will recall, are words pronounced alike but different in meaning and spelling. Example: *wait*, meaning "delay," and *weight*, meaning "heaviness."

Note the spelling in these sets of homonyms:

hoarse (harsh in sound): His voice sounded *hoarse*.
horse (the animal): Get off your *horse*.

hour (sixty minutes): An *hour* went by.
our (belonging to us): Are these *our* seats?

its (belonging to it): It (the cry) reached *its* topmost note.
it's (it is): Put on warm clothes; *it's* freezing.

know (be aware of): Do you *know* how to change a tire?
no (not any): The dogs evinced *no* inclination to stray.

meat (animal flesh used as food): *Meat* is scarce.
meet (come together): Let's *meet* at the game.

pale (not bright): A *pale* light is not good for painting.
pail (bucket): Pour some water into the *pail*.

peace (opposite of war): We must live in *peace*.
piece (fragment): A *piece* of flying metal cut his hand.

seam (line formed by the sewing together of two pieces of material): The skirt is coming apart at the *seams*.
seem (appear): We *seem* to be riding in the wrong direction.

scene (stage setting): In the second act, there is a change of *scene*.
seen (past participle of *to see*): Have you *seen* Mary's new hair-do?

sole (bottom of a shoe): This slipper has a thin *sole*.
sole (one and only): She was the *sole* survivor.
sole (the fish): For dinner they had filet of *sole*.
soul (spirit): It might have been a lost *soul* wailing.

their (belonging to them): *Their* house has been renovated.
there (in that place): You may leave your coats *there*.
there (used before a verb): *There* were several applicants for the position.
they're (they are): *They're* after us, Bill.

Complete each sentence below by inserting the correct homonym.

1. No one lives in the house except Mrs. Wiggins; she is the _____ tenant. (soul, sole)

2. I was so _____ I could hardly speak. (horse, hoarse)

3. _____ are four quarts in a gallon. (Their, There, They're)

4. The _____ is nearly over. (hour, our)

5. There can be no _____ until the dispute is settled. (piece, peace)

6. A taxi was nowhere to be _____. (scene, seen)

7. We did not _____ what had happened. (know, no)

8. A man's _____ is believed to be immortal. (sole, soul)

9. Here is a mop and a _____. (pale, pail)

10. Things are not what they _____. (seam, seem)

11. _____ too late now to do anything about it. (Its, It's)

12. Who would like another _____ of pie? (peace, piece)

13. Can you sew a straight _____? (seem, seam)

14. One of my sneakers has a hole in the _____. (soul, sole)

15. _____ are not many things for us to talk about. (They're, There, Their)

16. The _____ is the breakfast room of the Day family on Madison Avenue in the late 1880's. (scene, seen)

17. Please let us know when it's _____ turn. (our, hour)

18. The price of _____ soared last week. (meet, meat)

19. One of the dogs didn't get _____ fish. (it's, its)

20. The house was easily visible in the _____ moonlight. (pail, pale)

21. The dogs should be fed; _____ hungry. (they're, their, there)

22. She screamed herself _____ . (hoarse, horse)

23. Do you know where we are going to _____? (meet, meat)

24. There was no _____ on the menu. (sole, soul)

25. There are plenty of seats; there is _____ waiting. (no, know)

Correct Usage: Sticking to One Tense

"I took out six fish. One Ear didn't get no fish. I *come* back to the bag afterward an' got 'im his fish."

If we examine Bill's tenses, we find the following. He begins with the past tense—*took,* and continues with the past tense—*didn't get.* Then he shifts to the present tense—*come,* but ends by returning to the past tense—*got.*

Formal English does not permit us to shift tenses as Bill does. If we begin in the past tense, we must stick to the past tense; if we begin with the present, we must stick with the present.

If Jack London had wanted Bill to speak formal English, he would have written "I *came* back to the bag afterward and got him his fish." (He would also have written "One Ear didn't get *any* fish," avoiding the double negative, which likewise is not permitted in formal English.)

WRONG: The driver *stops* the bus and *told* everybody to get off.

RIGHT: The driver *stops* the bus and *tells* everybody to get off.

EXPLANATION: The first of the two parallel verbs is in the present tense—*stops.* Therefore, the second must also be in the present tense—*tells.* There is no reason to shift tenses.

WRONG: Ahead I *saw* a crowd. I *ran* over and *ask* what was wrong.

RIGHT: Ahead I *saw* a crowd. I *ran* over and *asked* what was wrong.

EXPLANATION: Since the story begins in the past tense—*saw, ran,* it should continue in the past tense—*asked.*

In the blank space insert the tense required by the sentence.

1. Just as I entered, someone _____ up and said, "Hi." (come, came)

2. Ken took a long lead off first and suddenly _____ toward second. (races, raced)

3. The president called the meeting to order. The secretary _____ the minutes. (read, reads)

4. Whenever I ask him to explain, he _____, "Later, not now." (says, said)

5. All of a sudden he cried "Lets go!" and _____ me by the arm. (pulled, pulls)

6. As we turned into Pell Street, the sun _____ up. (came, come)

7. He starts the engine and backs out the car. In a minute we _____ on the highway. (were, are)

8. As soon as Mom learned of our trip, she _____ to worry. (began, begins)

9. Play resumes and Josh _____ around right end for a seven-yard gain. (dashed, dashes)

10. He accused us of unfairness and _____ before we could answer. (leaves, left)

How old do you think you will be when you learn how to drive and own your first car? Bud Crayne realized both of these desires at a very tender age.

from

Hot Rod

by Henry Gregor Felsen

Bud Crayne was a lanky, raw-boned boy of seventeen with a long face, bold, self-confident black eyes, and a thin mouth that almost always held a challenging, reckless smile. He wore an old fedora hat with the brim turned up in front and fastened to the crown with a giant safety pin, a tight fitting black leather motor- 5 cycle jacket with zippers in the sides and sleeves and studded with metal buttons, and faded blue denim trousers. On his feet he wore short leather boots ornamented at the ankle with small brass chains.

Bud's parents had died when he was in grade school, and since 10 that time he had lived with a bachelor uncle who shared furnished quarters with his young nephew. At first the housekeeper where they lived had watched over Bud, made sure he wore clean clothes and ate his meals and left for school on time. Bud's uncle didn't know much about taking care of a boy, and let the housekeeper 15 take over. As long as Bud was well and out of trouble, his uncle didn't worry.

During his early years Bud enjoyed an unusual amount of independence. The more he could look after himself, the more he was allowed to. He stayed out late, roamed when and where 20 he wished, and learned a hard kind of self-reliance.

He had started hanging around Jake Clymer's garage almost at once. Jake let him stay, taught him about cars, and paid him

for his work. Bud's real interest in cars led him to spend more
and more time at Jake's, until, in his 'teens, he knew everything
about cars that Jake could teach him, plus a good deal he'd
learned himself out of books and magazines.

Bud had learned to drive while most boys were still struggling
with bicycles, and once given this head start behind the wheel,
he never relinquished it. He had always been able to out-drive
the others, and his leadership behind the wheel was seldom
questioned or (any more) challenged.

At seventeen Bud was his own boss, resented any attempts
by anyone to guide or counsel (he called it interfering with)
his ways, and he not only worked at Jake's, but practically
lived at the garage.

Growing up in this way without a family, Bud always felt
different from the other boys and girls in town, and was always
a little apart from them. When they turned to the warmth and
love in their homes, he, left alone, turned to the garage, and his
car. The hours that others spent with mothers, fathers, sisters
or brothers, Bud spent with his homemade hop-up. It was his
family. He was in the habit—like cowboys who rode lonesome
ranges for isolated days at a time and talked to their horses to
break the silence—of talking to his car as though it were animate,
and could understand, and sympathize.

His independence made him seem more mature than the other
boys his age who yet had to ask parental permission to come and
go. Bud regarded himself a man, and thought (he thought) like
a man. He had a job, and as soon as he was graduated from high
school, he was going to be Jake's partner in the garage. Content
with this future which assured him an income and a chance to
experiment with motors, he considered himself old enough to
marry. When high school was over with, and he was working full
time, he intended marrying LaVerne Shuler. Why not? He could
support a wife, and, for the first time in his life, he would have a
real home of his own.

Meanwhile, Bud worked for Jake in his free time. When he
wasn't working he was on the road. He tinkered with his car for
hours in order to have pleasant moments of speed on the highway. When he was behind the wheel, in control of his hopped-up
motor, he was king of the road. When he was happy, his happiness
reached its peak when he could express it in terms of speed and
roaring power, the pull of his engine, the whistle of the wind in
his ears, and the glorious sensation of free flight.

When he was unhappy, discontented, moody, the wheel again
offered him his answer. At these times there was solace and for-
getfulness behind the wheel. The motor snarled rather than sang,
speed became a lance rather than a banner, and revenge against
trouble was won through the conquest of other cars that accepted
his challenge to race. And when he was alone on the road, his
car and its speed seemed to remove him from the troubles that
plagued him while his feet had contact with the earth. Once re-

moved from bodily contact with the ground, once in motion, once
in a world of his own making, he escaped his troubles and sorrows 75
in speed, in the true touch of the wheel, in the trustworthy thunder
of the motor, the rushing sensation of detachment from all that
was rooted or planted in earth.

Understanding What You Have Read

In the blank space write the *letter* of the choice that best completes the statement.

1. The passage suggests that Bud ____.

    A. is something of a truant
    B. has no problems
    C. can read well
    D. accepts challenges, but does not challenge others

2. Bud regards advice from others ____.

    A. as an opportunity to learn
    B. as interference
    C. with an open mind
    D. with appreciation

3. The author ____.

    A. regards Bud as a man
    B. considers Bud old enough to marry
    C. agrees that Bud can think like a man
    D. suggests that Bud is lonely

4. Bud ____.

    A. is recognized for his leadership as a driver
    B. has learned all that he knows about cars from Jake Clymer
    C. has been an orphan since infancy
    D. wants to drop out of school

5. The author indicates that Bud does not ____.

    A. try to escape from his trouble
    B. enjoy speeding
    C. need revenge
    D. have a very happy life

Learning New Words

Line	Word	Meaning	Typical Use
45	**animate** *(adj.)* 'an-ə-mət	having life; living; alive	I was not the only *animate* being in the room; there were the goldfish, as well as some flies.
		(ant. **inanimate***)*	This feather was once part of a living creature, but now it is *inanimate*.
51	**content** *(adj.)* kən-'tent	not disposed to complain or grumble	We wouldn't think of moving because we are very *content* with our present neighborhood.
		(ant. **discontent, discontented***)*	Fred's father is going into business for himself because he is *discontent* with his job.
77	**detachment** *(n.)* di-'tach-mənt	act or process of *detaching* (separating); separation	On the road, a trailer must be securely linked to the towing vehicle to prevent *detachment*.
		(ant. **attachment***)*	The stray dog developed an *attachment* for us, following us wherever we went.
1	**lanky** *(adj.)* 'laŋ-kē	awkwardly tall and thin; bony; rawboned	The *lanky* youth could not qualify as a football lineman because he lacked the necessary weight.
		(ant. **burly, husky***)*	It was difficult to gain ground against our *burly* opponents, some of whom were 200 lbs. or more.
73	**plague** *(v.)* 'plāg	cause worry or distress to; vex; torment; harass	The road construction lasted two years and *plagued* drivers with dust, detours, and tie-ups.
3	**reckless** *(adj.)* 'rek-ləs	marked by a lack of caution; heedless; rash; careless	The motorist who ignored a red light and narrowly missed two cars was given a summons for *reckless* driving.
		(ant. **cautious***)*	A *cautious* driver makes a complete stop at a "Full Stop" sign and checks traffic in all directions before proceeding.

30	**relinquish** *(v.)* ri-'liŋ-kwish	give up; let go of; abandon	When the librarian asked me to *relinquish* the Spanish dictionary, I got her permission to keep it ten minutes longer.
		(ant. **keep***)*	
65	**sensation** *(n.)* sen-'sā-shən	feeling; awareness; consciousness produced by stimulation of the sense of sight, hearing, touch, smell, or taste	The rapid descent of the elevator gave me a *sensation* of falling.
67	**solace** *(n.)* 'säl-əs	alleviation of grief or anxiety; comfort; relief; consolation	Thank you for your cheerful "get-well" card; it was a great *solace* to me.
46	**sympathize** *(v.)* 'sim-pə-ˌthīz	1. share in suffering or grief; feel pity or compassion	I feel no pity for the reckless driver who caused the accident, but I *sympathize* with the people who were hurt.
		2. be in accord with; agree with	I *sympathize* with some of Pat's views, though I have not yet definitely decided to vote for her.

Applying What You Have Learned

I. Which of the two choices makes the sentence correct? Write the *letter* of the correct answer in the space provided.

1. He relinquished his seat ____.

A. and sat down   B. to an elderly lady

2. ____ are all animate.

A. Wood, metal, and glass   B. Trees, grass, and birds

3. The lanky freshman ____.

A. towers above his companions   B. is thirty pounds overweight

4. Most people are inclined to sympathize with the ____ fortunate.

A. more   B. less

5. The team has been plagued by a long string of ____.

A. victories   B. injuries

6. If you are content, why do you look so ____?

    A. hurt   B. pleased

7. Though your team lost, the fact that you ____ should give you some solace.

    A. scored two touchdowns   B. dropped the ball at the goal line

8. The reckless camper ____.

    A. cooked the evening meal over an   B. threw a lighted match into the brush
        outdoor grill

9. There is no sensation in ____.

    A. the limb of a dead tree   B. a bear cub's paw

10. Detachment of the stub is simple: just ____ on the dotted line.

    A. sign your name   B. tear it off

II. The meaning of each expression below can be found in the vocabulary list at the bottom of the exercise. Find that meaning and write it in the space provided.

_____ **1.** awkwardly tall and thin

_____ **2.** let go of

_____ **3.** act or process of separating

_____ **4.** share in suffering or grief

_____ **5.** marked by lack of caution

_____ **6.** alleviation of grief or anxiety

_____ **7.** having life

_____ **8.** consciousness produced by stimulation of a sense

_____ **9.** cause worry or distress to

_____ **10.** not disposed to complain or grumble

Vocabulary List

plague	lanky
content	sympathize
solace	reckless
sensation	animate
detachment	relinquish

III. Synonyms and Antonyms

Fill in the blanks in column A with the required synonyms and antonyms, selecting them from column B.

Column A		Column B
_____	1. antonym for *pleased*	sympathize
_____	2. synonym for *feel pity*	alive
_____	3. antonym for *keep*	plague
_____	4. synonym for *vex*	reckless
_____	5. antonym for *burly*	discontented
_____	6. synonym for *feeling*	detachment
_____	7. antonym for *cautious*	sensation
_____	8. antonym for *inanimate*	solace
_____	9. synonym for *separation*	relinquish
_____	10. synonym for *relief*	lanky

IV. Picture Quiz

In the space below, write the *letter* of the picture that best fits the meaning of the sentence.

1. Only ____ appears to be content.

2. Only ___ is animate.

3. Henry is so lanky, he reminds me of ___ .

Learning Some Derivatives

Each word in bold type below is a *root*. The words below it are its *derivatives*. Note that *animate,* when used as a verb, is pronounced ˈan-ə-ˌmāt.

animate *(adj.)*

The figure appeared to be a statue, but when it moved slightly, I knew it was *animate.*

animate *(v.)*

By asking an interesting question, you can *animate* a lifeless discussion.

animation *(n.)*

Your voice lacks liveliness. Put some *animation* into it.

content *(adj.)*

Peter was not *content* with his seat and asked the teacher to change it.

content *(v.)*

The teacher told Peter that, since she was busy, he would have to *content* himself with his assigned seat for a while.

contentment *(n.)*

Later, when she changed his seat, she could tell by his look of *contentment* that he was pleased.

detach *(v.)*	This coat has an extra lining for added warmth. It is easy to *detach*.
detachable *(adj.)*	The lining is *detachable*.
detachment *(n.)*	*Detachment* of the lining is no problem — simply zip it out.
plague *(n.)*	The *plague*, a deadly disease, killed millions of people during the Middle Ages.
plague *(v.)*	"These debts *plague* me," said Dad. "I wish I could find a way to pay them off."
reckless *(adj.)*	Becoming *reckless*, Phil raced across the traffic on Main Street, against the light.
recklessly *(adv.)*	Phil *recklessly* dodged one car after another to get to the other side of the street.
recklessness *(n.)*	Such *recklessness* sometimes results in a fatal accident.
solace *(n.)*	It was good to hear you say that you thought I should have been given the prize. Your words were a *solace* to me.
solace *(v.)*	Your kind words did much to *solace* me when I was feeling blue.
sympathy *(n.)*	In the coming election, Dad is going to vote for the Republicans, but Mother's *sympathy* is with the Democrats.
sympathetic *(adj.)*	Mother is *sympathetic* toward the views of the Democratic Party.
sympathetically *(adv.)*	Dad is *sympathetically* inclined toward the Republican Party platform.
sympathize *(v.)*	Mother *sympathizes* with the Democrats.
sympathizer *(n.)*	Dad is a Republican *sympathizer*.

Fill each blank below with the word in the list above that best fits the meaning of the sentence.

1. The bag has a(an) _____ shoulder strap that is very easy to take off or put back.

2. In the first inning, Tom pitched _____, walking three batters and making four wild pitches.

3. Jane wants the Bears to win, but I am a Red Sox _____.

4. The moral of the story is that sudden wealth may bring unhappiness instead of _____.

5. Yesterday you seemed lifeless, but today you are full of _____.

6. If you visit a patient too soon after his operation, you may annoy him rather than _____ him.

7. Most parents contribute to the Scholarship Fund because of their _____ with its goals.

8. Today we have the medical knowledge to deal effectively with any outbreak of the _____.

9. Our English teacher has a wonderful sense of humor, and he uses it to _____ his lessons.

10. Some people can never be satisfied; nothing will _____ them.

Improving Your Spelling: Problems of Final -Y

I. Attaching Suffixes

A. Look at the letter before final -Y. If it is a *consonant,* change the Y to I before attaching the suffix.

MARRY + ED = MARRIED
HAPPY + NESS = HAPPINESS
LANKY + EST = LANKIEST

B. However, do not change the -Y if the suffix begins with an I.

MARRY + ING = MARRYING
BABY + ISH = BABYISH
HOBBY + IST = HOBBYIST

C. If the letter before final -Y is a *vowel,* do not change the Y.

PLAY + ED = PLAYED
ENJOY + ABLE = ENJOYABLE
SURVEY + OR = SURVEYOR

D. Remember, however, that adding ED to *lay, pay, say,* and their compounds results in *laid, paid, said, mislaid, repaid, unsaid,* etc.

L A Y + E D = L A I D
P A Y + E D = P A I D
S A Y + E D = S A I D

E. Note, too, that *day + ly = daily.*

D A Y + L Y = D A I L Y

II. Forming Plurals

A. Look at the letter before final -Y. If it is a *vowel,* simply add S.

B O Y + S = B O Y S
H I G H W A Y + S = H I G H W A Y S
T U R K E Y + S = T U R K E Y S

B. If the letter before final -Y is a *consonant,* change the Y to I and add ES.

F A M I L Y + E S = F A M I L I E S
S T O R Y + E S = S T O R I E S
L A D Y + E S = L A D I E S

A. Fill in the blanks.

1. unhappy + est   = _____

2. employ + able   = _____

3. plural of *key*   = _____

4. boy + ish   = _____

5. destroy + ed   = _____

6. plural of *city*   = _____

7. fry + ed   = _____

8. worry + ing = _____

9. plural of *delay* = _____

10. early + er = _____

11. overlay + ed = _____

12. plural of *attorney* = _____

13. employ + ment = _____

14. lobby + ist = _____

15. plural of *liberty* = _____

16. stay + ed = _____

17. underpay + ed = _____

18. plural of *ally* = _____

19. plural of *company* = _____

20. day + ly = _____

B. Fill in the blanks.

1. grayish − ish = _____

2. hurried − ed = _____

3. singular of *alleys* = _____

4. prepaid − ed = _____

5. terrifying − ing = _____

6. singular of *necessities* = _____

7. delayed − ed = _____

8. bodily − ly = _____

9. singular of *landladies* = _____

10. lonelier − er = _____

Correct Usage: Some Expressions to Avoid

The verb *graduate* is usually followed by *from*:

"He had a job, and as soon as he was *graduated from* high school, he was going to be Jake's partner in the garage."

1. AVOID: My brother *graduated* high school.
   SAY: My brother *graduated from* high school.
   OR SAY: My brother *was graduated from* high school.

The adjective *different* is usually followed by *from,* rather than *than:*

"... Bud always felt *different from* the other boys ..."

2. AVOID: Astronomy is *different than* astrology.
   SAY: Astronomy is *different from* astrology.

Here are some further expressions for you to avoid.

3. AVOID: The game will be played *irregardless* of the weather.
   SAY: The game will be played *regardless* of the weather.

4. AVOID: Please get *off of* the field.
   SAY: Please get *off* the field.

5. AVOID: Ira is six *foot* tall.
   SAY: Ira is six *feet* tall.

6. AVOID: *Me and my friend* had a quarrel.
   SAY: *My friend and I* had a quarrel.

7. AVOID: You should *try and* do better.
   SAY: You should *try to* do better.

8. AVOID: The *reason* is *because* I was sick.
   SAY: The *reason* is *that* I was sick.

9. AVOID: We had a *real* good time.
   SAY: We had a *really* good time.

10. AVOID: *This here* book is all about hockey.
    SAY: *This* book is all about hockey.

If the sentence is incorrect, rewrite it correctly in the space provided. If the sentence is correct, write "Correct." (Two of the sentences are correct.)

1. After failing Spanish, Nora promised she would try and do better.

_____

_____

2. The reason is that we had a flat tire.

_____

_____

3. If you need something, buy it irregardless of the cost.

_____

_____

4. Your answer is different than mine.

_____

_____

5. When did your sister graduate high school?

_____

_____

6. She is five feet tall and has brown hair.

_____

_____

7. Kindly take your feet off of that chair.

_____

_____

8. That was a real good book.

_____

_____

9. This here pie is delicious.

_____

_____

10. Me and my brother get along well.

_____

_____

READING SELECTION 16

Were you ever lost? Did you ever try to help someone who was lost?

Late one night about 150 years ago in the city of London, a pretty little girl who has lost her way stops a stranger to ask for directions.

from

The Old Curiosity Shop

by Charles Dickens

One night I had roamed into the City, and was walking slowly on in my usual way, musing upon a great many things, when I was arrested by an inquiry, the purport of which did not reach me, but which seemed to be addressed to myself, and was proffered in a soft sweet voice that struck me very pleasantly. I 5 turned hastily round and found at my elbow a pretty little girl, who begged to be directed to a certain street at a considerable distance, and indeed in quite another quarter of the town.

"It's a very long way from here," said I, "my child."

"I know that, Sir," she replied timidly. "I am afraid it is a 10 very long way, for I came from there tonight."

"Alone?" said I, in some surprise.

"Oh yes, I don't mind that, but I am a little frightened now, for I had lost my road."

"And what made you ask it of me? Suppose I should tell you 15 wrong."

"I am sure you will not do that," said the little creature, "you are such a very old gentleman, and walk so slow yourself."

I cannot describe how much I was impressed by this appeal and the energy with which it was made, which brought a tear 20 into the child's clear eye, and made her slight figure tremble as she looked up into my face.

"Come," said I, "I'll take you there."

She put her hand in mine as confidingly as if she had known
25 me from her cradle, and we trudged away together: the little
creature accommodating her pace to mine, and rather seeming to
lead and take care of me than I to be protecting her. I observed
that every now and then she stole a curious look at my face as if
to make quite sure that I was not deceiving her, and that these
30 glances (very sharp and keen they were too) seemed to increase
her confidence at every repetition.

For my part, my curiosity and interest were at least equal to
the child's, for child she certainly was, although I thought it
probable from what I could make out, that her very small and
35 delicate frame imparted a peculiar youthfulness to her appearance. Though more scantily attired than she might have been,
she was dressed with perfect neatness, and betrayed no marks of
poverty or neglect.

"Who has sent you so far by yourself?" said I.
40 "Somebody who is very kind to me, Sir."
"And what have you been doing?"
"That, I must not tell," said the child firmly.

There was something in the manner of this reply which caused
me to look at the little creature with an involuntary expression
45 of surprise; for I wondered what kind of errand it might be that
occasioned her to be prepared for questioning. Her quick eye
seemed to read my thoughts, for as it met mine she added that
there was no harm in what she had been doing, but it was a
great secret—a secret which she did not even know herself.
50 This was said with no appearance of cunning or deceit, but
with an unsuspicious frankness that bore the impress of truth.

Understanding What You Have Read

In the blank space, write the *letter* of the choice that best completes the statement.

1. The narrator ____.

A. first notices the child when she tugs at his elbow
B. hears the child's voice before he sees her
C. sees the child before she sees him
D. seems to be hard of hearing

2. The child ____.

A. is completely without fear
B. walks more slowly than the narrator
C. appears highly intelligent
D. hesitates before answering questions

3. The narrator _____.

    A. suspects that the child is lying
    B. is not used to walking slowly
    C. is not surprised that the child has made a long trip by herself
    D. seems to know his way around town

4. When asked what she has been doing, the child _____.

    A. indicates she has not been doing anything wrong
    B. tells all she knows
    C. remains silent
    D. invents an obvious lie

5. The word *betrayed,* as used in the passage on line 37 ("she was dressed with perfect neatness, and *betrayed* no marks of poverty or neglect"), means _____.

    A. treacherously disclosed
    B. concealed
    C. showed
    D. covered up

Learning New Words

Line	Word	Meaning	Typical Use
26	**accommodate** *(v.)* ə-'käm-ə-ˌdāt	1. adapt; adjust; make fit	When we moved, it did not take me long to *accommodate* myself to my new school.
		2. have space for; hold without crowding; contain	The new hotel can *accommodate* two hundred guests.
19	**appeal** *(n.)* ə-'pēl	earnest request; plea; call for help	Dozens of volunteers responded to the hospital's *appeal* for blood donors.
36	**attire** *(v.)* ə-'tī(ə)r	put garments on; clothe; dress	On special occasions like graduations and weddings, people *attire* themselves in their very best clothes.
31	**confidence** *(n.)* 'kän-fəd-ən(t)s	feeling of trust; faith; reliance	You may have *confidence* in what my brother has promised, for he always keeps his word.
		(ant. **doubt, apprehension**)	I have no *apprehension* about lending my science notes to Selma, as I have absolute trust in her.

32	**curiosity** *(n.)* ˌkyu̇r-ē-'äs-ət-ē	1. eager desire to know; inquisitiveness	You can satisfy your *curiosity* about Lauren's absence by calling her and asking why she has not been in school.
		2. strange or rare object; article valued for its strangeness or rarity	There are many people who visit antique shops in search of *curiosities.*
50	**deceit** *(n.)* di-'sēt	act of *deceiving* (misleading); dishonest trick; cheating; lying	The wise dealer treats his customers fairly because he knows that in the long run *deceit* does not pay.
		(ant. **honesty***)*	
35	**delicate** *(adj.)* 'del-i-kət	easily hurt or damaged; weak; frail; sickly	If you drop your watch, you will almost certainly damage it, as it has a very *delicate* mechanism.
51	**frankness** *(n.)* 'fraŋk-nəs	openness and honesty in expressing what one thinks; outspokenness	I appreciate your *frankness* in telling me that this jacket does not fit me. It's good to know the truth, even if it hurts.
		(ant. **reticence, silence***)*	Some of my friends said nothing when they saw me in this jacket, and by their *reticence* they led me to believe that it looks good on me.
44	**involuntary** *(adj.)* (')in-'väl-ən-ˌter-ē	not subject to control by the will; automatic; instinctive	We cannot stop a sneeze or a yawn because they are *involuntary* acts.
		(ant. **voluntary***)*	My decision to quit was entirely *voluntary*; I left because I wanted to.
10	**timidly** *(adv.)* 'tim-əd-lē	in a *timid* (fearful) manner; fearfully; shyly; hesitantly	When it seemed that there might be a fight, most of the bystanders *timidly* withdrew to safe ground.
		(ant. **valiantly, courageously***)*	Our leader, however, *valiantly* remained on the scene in an attempt to get both sides to talk things over.

216

Applying What You Have Learned

I. Which of the two choices makes the sentence correct? Write the *letter* of the correct answer in the space provided.

1. ____ is usually an involuntary remark.

   A. "O. K."　　　　　　　　　　B. "Ouch!"

2. To ____ is to practice deceit.

   A. pretend to be older than you are　　B. come late to a quiz

3. The salesman was attired ____.

   A. after a long day　　　　　B. in a business suit

4. An ____ is an appeal with which most of us are familiar.

   A. S. O. S.　　　　　　　　　B. I. O. U.

5. I was ____ to follow the path as my eyes accommodated themselves to the dark.

   A. unable　　　　　　　　　　B. able

6. If you behave timidly, others may think you are ____.

   A. rude　　　　　　　　　　　B. scared

7. Her curiosity shows that she is ____.

   A. eager to learn　　　　　　B. not interested

8. A ____ is extremely delicate.

   A. spider's web　　　　　　　B. mountain top

9. George must have confidence in you, for he ____.

   A. gave you the combination to his locker　　B. has never borrowed a thing from you

10. The child's frankness ____.

    A. prevented us from learning the secret　　B. helped us to get at the facts

II. The meaning of each expression below can be found in the vocabulary list at the bottom of the exercise. Find that meaning and write it in the space provided.

_____ 1. feeling of trust

_____ 2. have space for

_____ 3. openness in expressing what one thinks

_____ 4. in a fearful manner

_____ 5. easily hurt or damaged

_____ 6. put garments on

_____ 7. not subject to control by the will

_____ 8. eager desire to know

_____ 9. call for help

_____ 10. act of misleading

Vocabulary List

curiosity	appeal
attire	timidly
involuntary	confidence
deceit	frankness
accommodate	delicate

III. **Synonyms and Antonyms**

Fill the blanks in column A with the required synonyms or antonyms, selecting them from column B.

Column A   *Column B*

_____ 1. antonym for *apprehension*   delicate

_____ 2. synonym for *frail*   voluntary

_____ 3. antonym for *valiantly*   appeal

_____ 4. synonym for *adjust*   confidence

_____ 5. antonym for *honesty*   attire

_____ 6. synonym for *plea*   accommodate

_____ 7. antonym for *reticence*   timidly

_____ 8. synonym for *clothe*   curiosity

_____ 9. antonym for *instinctive*   frankness

_____ 10. synonym for *inquisitiveness*   deceit

IV. Picture Quiz

In the space below, write the *letter* of the picture that best fits the meaning of the sentence.

1. One of the best ways to satisfy your curiosity is to go to a ____.

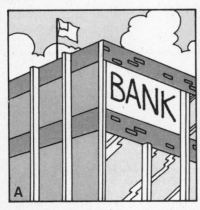  

2. ____ can keep you well attired.

3. ____ is delicate.

Learning Some Derivatives

Each word in bold type below is a *root*. The words below it are its *derivatives*.

accommodate *(v.)*   The Seaside Inn can *accommodate* eighty-four guests.

accommodation *(n.)*   The Seaside Inn has *accommodations* for eighty-four guests.

appeal *(n.)*   If found guilty, a defendant may make an *appeal* to a higher tribunal.

appeal *(v.)*   If found guilty, a defendant may *appeal* to a higher court.

attire *(v.)*   Parents usually *attire* their children in new clothes for the first day of school.

attire *(n.)*   Many students arrive in new *attire* on the first day of school.

confide *(v.)*   A defendant must *confide* in his lawyer. Whom else is he to trust?

confident *(adj.)*   A defendant has to feel *confident* that his attorney will not let him down.

confidently *(adv.)*   He should *confidently* tell his lawyer everything, without fear that he will be betrayed.

confidential *(adj.)*   He should have so much trust in his lawyer as to be able to give him the most *confidential* information.

confidentially *(adv.)*   He should be able to tell his attorney *confidentially* things that he would tell to no one else.

confidence *(n.)*   A defendant must have *confidence* in his lawyer.

curious *(adj.)*   I showed no interest in the seashell, but Peter was *curious* about it.

curiously *(adv.)*   He examined it *curiously*.

curiosity *(n.)*   His *curiosity* prompted him to look up seashells in the encyclopedia.

deceive *(v.)*   Why do you suspect Stan of lying? What reason can he have to *deceive* you?

deceiver *(n.)*   He has always told the truth. He is not a *deceiver*.

deceit *(n.)*   I have never known him to practice *deceit*.

deceitful *(adj.)*   I have never known Stan to be *deceitful*.

deceitfully *(adv.)*   If he did misinform you, he must have done it accidentally, not *deceitfully*.

deception *(n.)*   I cannot believe that Stan would be guilty of *deception*.

delicate *(adj.)*	This camera is a *delicate* instrument. Handle it with care.
delicately *(adv.)*	This camera may break if dropped. It is *delicately* constructed.
delicacy *(n.)*	Use extreme caution in handling equipment of such *delicacy*.
frank *(adj.)*	Since you have asked me to be *frank*, I must tell you that you are selfish.
frankly *(adv.)*	I tell you *frankly* that, if you do not change, you will lose all your friends, including me.
frankness *(n.)*	My *frankness* may hurt you, but you have asked for the truth, and I have given it to you.
involuntary *(adj.)*	My eyes blink when a flashbulb goes off. It is an *involuntary* reaction.
involuntarily *(adv.)*	My eyes blink *involuntarily* when a flashbulb goes off.
timid *(adj.)*	Jump in. The water can't hurt you. Don't be *timid*.
timidly *(adv.)*	Don't stand so *timidly* at the edge of the pool. The water is fine. Jump in.
timidity *(n.)*	I, too, was once afraid of the water, but I got over my *timidity*. You can, too.

Fill each blank below with the word listed above that best fits the meaning of the sentence.

1. Are they telling the truth, or are they trying to _____ us?

2. Gossips are _____ about other people's business.

3. I walked up to the microphone _____; I was scared.

4. Motel after motel flashed the "No Vacancy" sign; it was very hard to find a(an) _____ .

5. Let me ask you to be perfectly _____ and not to hold back any information.

6. My teeth chattered _____; it was so cold!

7. Pictures will be taken at the wedding; wear your best _____ .

8. Jean's health is of such _____ that she will have to remain at home for at least another month.

9. What I have told you is not _____ ; you may reveal it to anyone you wish.

10. Should our expenses continue to go up, we shall have to _____ to our members for an increase in dues.

Improving Your Spelling: Some Troublesome Derivatives

A few derivatives are difficult to spell because they unexpectedly drop or change one or two letters present in the root.

ROOT	DERIVATIVE	
curious	curiosity	(u dropped)
generous	generosity	(u dropped)
four	forty	(u dropped) Note, however: fourteen, fourth.
denounce	denunciation	(o dropped)
pronounce	pronunciation	(o dropped)
courteous	courtesy	(ou dropped)
argue	argument	(e dropped)
awe	awful	(e dropped)
disaster	disastrous	(e dropped)
enter	entrance	(e dropped)
hinder	hindrance	(e dropped)
monster	monstrous	(e dropped)
nine	ninth	(e dropped) Note, however: nineteen, ninety.
proceed	procedure	(e dropped)
remember	remembrance	(e dropped)
detain	detention	(ai becomes e)
maintain	maintenance	(ai becomes e)
retain	retention	(ai becomes e)
prevail	prevalent	(i dropped)
till	until	(l dropped)

222

I. Fill in the blanks in column C. Follow the sample:

	(A)	(B)	(C)
	Root	+ Suffix =	Derivative
	disaster	+ ous	= **disastrous**

1. four + ty = _____

2. nine + ty = _____

3. generous + ity = _____

4. maintain + ance = _____

5. courteous + y = _____

6. nine + th = _____

7. four + th = _____

8. enter + ance = _____

9. awe + ful = _____

10. prevail + ent = _____

II. Fill in the blanks in column B.

(A) Derivative	(B) Root
pronunciation	**pronounce**

1. hindrance _____

2. until _____

3. detention _____

4. awful _____

5. curiosity _____

6. procedure _____

7. denunciation _____

8. argument _____

9. remembrance _____

10. retention _____

Grammar: Compound Subjects

1. A *compound subject* (a subject consisting of two or more words connected by *and*) usually takes a plural verb.

> "For my part, my <u>curiosity and interest</u> <u>were</u> (not *was*) at least equal to the child's. . ."

> <u>Milk, butter, and cheese</u> <u>need</u> (not *needs*) to be kept in the refrigerator.

2. However, use a singular verb if the two words in the compound subject refer to the same person or thing.

> The <u>owner and operator</u> of the vehicle <u>is</u> (not *are*) Chester A. Banks.

> The <u>capital and largest city</u> of Massachusetts <u>is</u> (not *are*) Boston.

3. Also, use a singular verb if the compound subject is considered as a single thing, rather than two distinct things.

> <u>Spaghetti and meatballs</u> <u>was</u> not on the menu.
> (*Spaghetti and meatballs* is a single dish.)

> <u>Law and order</u> <u>has</u> to be maintained at all costs.
> (*Law and order* is a single idea.)

Each sentence below has a compound subject. Select the verb for that subject and write it in the blank space.

1. Radio and television *(help, helps)* _____ to keep us informed.

2. The patient's pulse and temperature *(has, have)* _____ been normal all day.

3. Ham and eggs *(is, are)* _____ served at breakfast.

4. When *(is, are)* _____ Paul and Eric leaving?

5. The winner and new champion *(was, were)* _____ acclaimed at the end of the bout.

6. Abraham and Straus *(is, are)* _____ a leading department store.

7. Your work and conduct *(needs, need)* _____ improvement.

8. The sum and substance of the matter *(is, are)* _____ that we are running out of cash.

9. Macaroni and cheese *(is, are)* _____ today's luncheon special.

10. Bud's speed and experience *(makes, make)* _____ him our most valuable player.

REVIEW OF GROUP IV

I. Fill in the missing letters of the words at the right of the definition. Then write the complete word in the blank space.

DEFINITION	WORD	COMPLETE WORD
1. not subject to control by the will	INVOLUN _ _ _ _	_____
2. grow dim	_ _ DE	_____
3. hold without crowding	ACC _ _ _ _ _ DATE	_____
4. number of similar things grouped together	_ _ _ STER	_____
5. feel pity or compassion	SYM _ _ _ _ _ IZE	_____
6. heavy of body	_ _ _ TLY	_____
7. conclude from known facts	DED _ _ _	_____
8. pass through or over	_ _ _ VERSE	_____
9. act of separating	DE _ _ _ _ MENT	_____
10. eager desire to know	_ _ _ IOSITY	_____
11. quarrel over petty things	BIC _ _ _	_____
12. become worn or ragged	_ _ AY	_____
13. call for help	PL _ _	_____
14. cause worry or distress to	_ _ _ GUE	_____
15. hand-operated	MAN _ _ _	_____
16. being the only one of its kind	_ NIQ _ _	_____
17. move upward	SO _ _	_____
18. not disposed to grumble	_ _ _ TENT	_____
19. easily damaged	DELIC _ _ _ _	_____
20. alleviation of grief	_ _ LACE	_____

II. To each line below, add a word that has the *same meaning* as the first two words on the line. Choose your words from the vocabulary list below.

1. clothe, dress, _____

2. awareness, feeling, _____

3. tale, story, _____

4. patron, customer, _____

5. coolly, calmly, _____

6. rash, heedless, _____

7. show, reveal, _____

8. alive, living, _____

9. consequence, importance, _____

10. embellishment, decoration, _____

Vocabulary List

evince	client
significance	narrative
ornament	attire
animate	dispassionately
sensation	reckless

III. For each italicized word in Column A, write the best *antonym* from Column B.

Column A   *Column B*

_____ 1. will probably *desist*   relinquish

_____ 2. the *burly* doorman   commonplace

_____ 3. proceeded *valiantly*   frankness

_____ 4. a *lowly* public servant   confidence

_____ 5. *deny* the fact   persist

_____ 6. an *extraordinary* event   timidly

_____ 7. complete *reticence*   honestly

_____ **8.** _keep_ everything   lanky

_____ **9.** deal _deceitfully_   acknowledge

_____ **10.** a feeling of _apprehension_   pompous

IV. **A.** From the derivative in column A, remove the prefix and/or suffix in column B, and write the root word in column C. Study the three examples that follow.

Column A	*Column B*		*Column C*
(DERIVATIVE)	— (PREFIX and/or SUFFIX)	=	(ROOT WORD)
incompatible	— in	=	**compatible**
generosity	— ity	=	**generous**
displacement	— dis _and_ ment	=	**place**
1. inanimate	— in	=	_____
2. accommodation	— ion	=	_____
3. unhappiness	— un _and_ ness	=	_____
4. curiosity	— ity	=	_____
5. dispassionate	— dis _and_ ate	=	_____
6. remembrance	— ance	=	_____
7. confidence	— ence	=	_____
8. impatiently	— im _and_ ly	=	_____
9. reducible	— ible	=	_____
10. portliness	— ness	=	_____

B. To the root in column A, add the suffix in column B, and write the derivative in column C. Study the sample.

Column A	*Column B*		*Column C*
(ROOT)	+ (SUFFIX)	=	(DERIVATIVE)
curious	+ ity	=	**curiosity**
1. maintain	+ ance	=	_____
2. argue	+ ment	=	_____
3. courteous	+ y	=	_____

4. nine + teen = _____

5. disaster + ous = _____

6. four + ty = _____

7. prevail + ent = _____

8. generous + ity = _____

9. detain + tion = _____

10. proceed + ure = _____

C. Insert the correct homonym.

1. Can you ride a _____ *(hoarse, horse)*?

2. Flounder, salmon, and _____ *(soul, sole)* are in good supply.

3. Where shall we _____ *(meat, meet)*?

4. The dog raised _____ *(it's, its)* ears.

5. Will you be _____ *(they're, their, there)*?

D. Fill in the blanks.

1. pay + ment = _____

2. plural of *necessity* = _____

3. burly + er = _____

4. singular of *enemies* = _____

5. gloomy + est = _____

6. plural of *bay* = _____

7. hurry + ing = _____

8. repay + ed = _____

9. plural of *alley* = _____

10. baby + ish = _____

V. Complete each sentence below with the most appropriate word from the following vocabulary list.

Vocabulary List

commonplace	content	confidence
attire	unique	appeal
soar	sympathize	relinquish
evince	animate	bicker

1. I _____ with the losers. Don't you feel sorry for them, too?

2. We thought Pat would like the flowers, but she did not _____ any enthusiasm for them.

3. Why don't you have _____ in the dean? Everybody else trusts him.

4. In walked Jeffrey, all dressed up in his finest holiday _____.

5. Let's not _____ about the batting order. You can bat first, if you insist.

6. Andrea was not _____; everyone else seemed satisfied.

7. Scoring the highest mark has become _____ for Russ. He does it all the time.

8. When Mrs. Goodman got on the crowded bus, I thought I should _____ my seat to her.

9. It was long believed that there is life on the moon, but no _____ creatures have been found there.

10. You will not find another player like Mark anywhere; he is _____.

VI. On lines B and C, write the required forms of the italicized word on line A.

1. A. We thought you were honest, not *deceitful*.

B. We never expected you to _____ us.

C. Who would have guessed that you could be such a sly _____?

2. A. You may lose much more than your license if you drive *recklessly*.

B. _____ drivers may lose their lives.

C. Overcome your _____.

3. A. If you keep breaking traffic laws and get hurt, don't expect any *sympathy*.

B. No one will be _____.

C. We will not _____ with you.

4. A. Some people always complain. Nothing can *content* them.

B. They can never find peace and _____.

C. They will never be _____.

5. A. Don't try to spare my feelings. Be *frank*.

B. Speak _____.

C. I prefer _____.

6. A. It was a simple graduation ceremony, without *pomp*.

B. The graduates did not wear caps and gowns, nor did they march _____ down the aisle.

C. There were no _____ speeches.

7. A. The information you give your physician is *confidential;* he will not reveal it to anyone else without your permission.

B. You may _____ in your physician.

C. You may have _____ in your physician.

8. A. Monica is good in *narration*.

B. When she tells a story, everybody listens. She is a skillful

_____.

C. She knows how to _____.

9. A. Does your little brother bother you *persistently*?

B. It is hard to put up with _____ nagging.

C. If my brother were to _____ in making a nuisance of himself, I wouldn't stand for it.

10. A. A doorknob makes it possible for us to open and close a door. It also serves as *ornamentation*.

B. A well-designed metal knob adds beauty to a wooden door; it is an attractive _____.

C. Doorknobs have both practical and _____ uses.

11. A. Don't be *timid*. There is nothing to be afraid of.

B. The dog won't bite you. Don't act so _____.

C. Get rid of your _____.

12. A. When Santa Claus emerged from the helicopter, the children eyed him *curiously*.

B. They gave him _____ glances.

C. They observed him with _____.

13. A. Though Sharon is a talented skater, she knows she is not *unique*.

B. She does not claim to be _____ talented; she acknowledges that others may skate as well, or even better.

C. She makes no claim to _____.

14. A. A gain of 25% is *significant*.

B. A gain of 5% does not usually mean much, but an improvement of 25% has real _____.

C. Your marks have improved _____ since our last talk.

15. A. The student actors were lifeless; they did not seem *animate*.

B. What can we do to _____ their acting?

C. How can we put some _____ into the play?

16. A. The patient's health is of such *delicacy* that he is not per-

mitted to have too many visitors.

B. When I greeted him, he smiled so _____

that it was obvious to me that he was still weak.

C. The patient is in _____ health.

17. A. My winter jacket has a *detachable* hood.

B. On warm days, I _____ the hood.

C. _____ is easy; the hood zips out. Attach-

ment is more difficult.

18. A. Marie is *confident* that she can win the election.

B. She _____ expects to be declared the

winner.

C. She has a great deal of self-_____ .

19. A. From their investigation, the detectives have been able

to *deduce* that the thief must have known the combination

to the safe.

B. Also _____ is the fact that the burglar

must have worn gloves; he left no fingerprints.

C. The detectives are going over the evidence to see if any

further _____ can be made.

20. A. If I could vote, I would cast my ballot for Simpson. I am

sympathetically inclined to his views.

B. My _____ is with Simpson.

C. I am a Simpson _____ .

INDEX